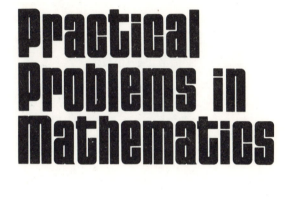

Practical Problems in Mathematics

FOR
Machinists

D0022836

Practical Problems in Mathematics

FOR
Machinists

JOHN G. BRADLEY

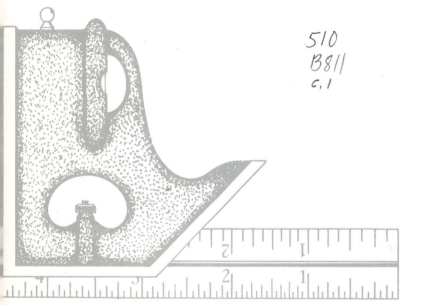

510
B811
c.1

DELMAR PUBLISHERS
COPYRIGHT © 1973
BY LITTON EDUCATIONAL PUBLISHING, INC.

All rights reserved. No part of this work covered by the copyright hereon may be reproduced or used in any form or by any means — graphic, electronic, or mechanical, including photocopying, recording, taping, or information storage and retrieval systems — without written permission of the publisher.

LIBRARY OF CONGRESS CATALOG CARD NUMBER: 72 - 174888

PRINTED IN THE UNITED STATES OF AMERICA
PUBLISHED SIMULTANEOUSLY IN CANADA BY
DELMAR PUBLISHERS, A DIVISION OF
VAN NOSTRAND REINHOLD, LTD.

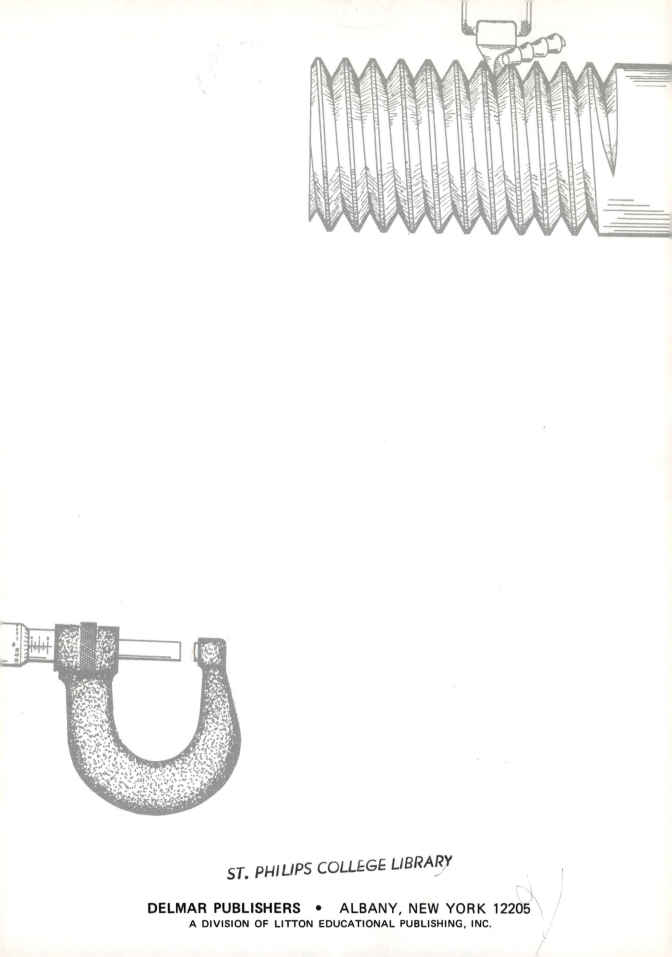

ST. PHILIPS COLLEGE LIBRARY

DELMAR PUBLISHERS • ALBANY, NEW YORK 12205

A DIVISION OF LITTON EDUCATIONAL PUBLISHING, INC.

CONTENTS

SECTION 7 RATIO AND PROPORTION

SECTION 8 PRACTICAL MEASUREMENTS

SECTION 9 FORMULAS

SECTION 10 GEOMETRIC CONSTRUCTIONS

49754

SECTION 11 GRAPHS

SECTION 12A TRIGONOMETRY

SECTION 12B OBLIQUE TRIANGLES

SECTION 13 BELT DRIVES AND GEAR TRAINS

SECTION 14 GEAR COMPUTATIONS

SECTION 15 LATHE WORK

The author and editorial staff at Delmar Publishers are interested in continually improving the quality of this instructional material. The reader is invited to submit constructive criticism and questions. Responses will be reviewed jointly by the author and source editor. Send comments to:

Editor-in-Chief
Box 5087
Albany, New York 12205

SECTION 1 — WHOLE NUMBERS

Unit 1 ADDITION OF WHOLE NUMBERS

BASIC PRINCIPLES OF ADDITION

- Study unit 1 in *Basic Mathematics Simplified* for the principles of addition, as applied to whole numbers.

- Apply the principles of addition to the work of the machinist, by solving the Review Problems which follow.

REVIEW PROBLEMS

1. What is the combined weight of the six machines shown in the diagram? _____

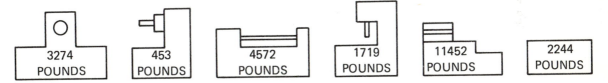

| 3274 POUNDS | 453 POUNDS | 4572 POUNDS | 1719 POUNDS | 11452 POUNDS | 2244 POUNDS |

2. The following lengths are cut from 20-foot bars of hot rolled steel: 221 inches, 197 inches, 34 inches, 107 inches, 116 inches, 231 inches, 239 inches, and 146 inches. How many inches of bar have been cut off? _____

3. A plant guard makes his tour of duty by patrolling the route shown on the diagram. What is the total distance he walks? _____

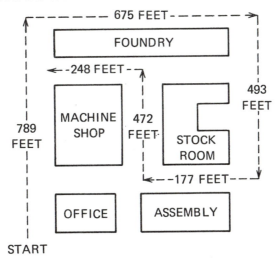

4. An automatic screw machine uses the following material: 42 lengths of 1-inch stock, 249 lengths of 3/4-inch stock, 377 lengths of 5/8-inch stock, 928 lengths of 1/2-inch stock, and 1015 lengths of 1/4-inch stock. What is the total length of material required? _____

5. A job ticket for a die job shows the hours spent in machining, as listed on the diagram. What is the total time required for this job?

_____

TIME CARD	
JOB *die shoe*	
Machine	**Hours**
Lathe	143
Milling	246
Grinder	47
Heat Treat	15
Total Hours	

6. On a stock room shelf, there are 5 milling cutters, 17 cut off tools, 23 spur gears, and 49 mill files. How many items are on the shelf?

_____

7. A machinist turns in time cards for four different jobs. These jobs take 632, 945, 89, and 665 minutes to complete. How many minutes does it take to complete all four jobs?

_____

8. Find distances A, B, C, and D.

_____

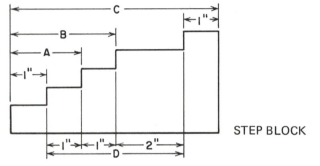

STEP BLOCK

9. Find the length of A, B, C, and D.

_____

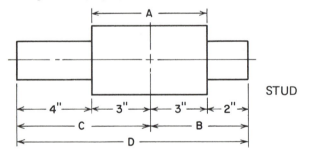

STUD

10. Five 1/4-inch holes are drilled in a 1/4" x 2" x 20" piece of cold rolled steel.

   a.   What is the total length between the outside holes?

_____

   b.   How far is the center hole from the right end?

_____

   c.   How far is hole A from the right end?

_____

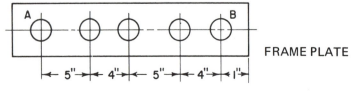

FRAME PLATE

11. A typical threaded bolt is shown. The designation 1/2″ — 13 NC means 13 threads per inch on a 1/2-inch diameter. This is a combination of diameter and thread known as National Coarse (NC).

    a.   Determine the overall length of the bolt.   _____

    b.   How long is the threaded portion?   _____

    c.   Give the thickness of the head.   _____

    d.   How long is the bolt, excluding the head?   _____

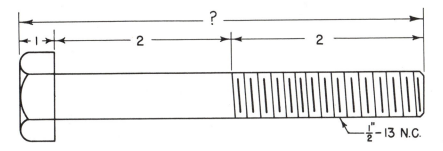

12. Five numbered shafts, like the one shown, vary in size. The chart lists the dimensions of each shaft in inches.

    a.   Determine the overall length X of each shaft in inches, using the measurements given in the chart.   _____

    b.   What is the total length of the five shafts?   _____

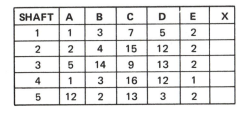

SHAFT	A	B	C	D	E	X
1	1	3	7	5	2	
2	2	4	15	12	2	
3	5	14	9	13	2	
4	1	3	16	12	1	
5	12	2	13	3	2	

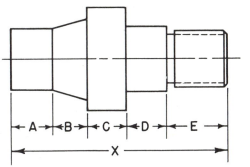

13. The following items are stocked in a tool crib: 239 tool bits, 347 drills, 562 washers, 747 cotter pins, and 658 Whitney keys. Find the total number of items.   _____

14. Several pieces are to be cut from a 1-inch diameter rod. The lengths needed are 7 inches, 12 inches, 14 inches, 31 inches, and 3 inches. How long a rod is required?   _____

15. Five pieces are cut from a piece of stock: 11 inches, 19 inches, 13 inches, 23 inches, and 15 inches. What is the total length?   _____

Unit 2 SUBTRACTION OF WHOLE NUMBERS

BASIC PRINCIPLES OF SUBTRACTION

- Study unit 2 in *Basic Mathematics Simplified* for the principles of subtraction, as applied to whole numbers.
- Apply the principles of subtraction to the work of the machinist, by solving the Review Problems which follow.

REVIEW PROBLEMS

1. A stock rack holds 4763 feet of 1-inch stock. A machinist uses 2895 feet. How much stock is left? _____

2. Four pieces measuring 49 inches, 72 inches, 27 inches, and 36 inches are cut from a steel bar measuring 192 inches long. A total of 1 inch is wasted in cutting. How much is left of the original bar? _____

3. Which is larger, the sum of 239, 473, 892, 652, and 378, or the sum of 972, 643, 179, 233, and 462? By how much? _____

4. A tank holds 275 gallons of cutting oil when full. A workman fills four containers which hold the amounts shown on the diagram. How much oil must be ordered to refill the tank? _____

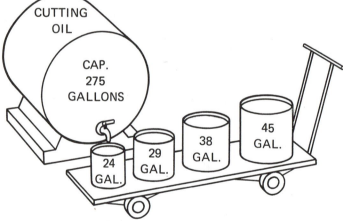

5. What is the size of the diameter of the hole in the washer? _____

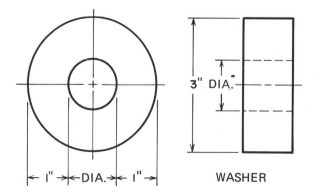

WASHER

6. a. Find distance A. _____

   b. What is the depth of the dovetail? _____

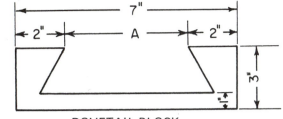

DOVETAIL BLOCK

7. a. Find the width across the top of the slide. _____

   b. What is the minimum depth of the slide that will fit the block _____
   shown in question 6?

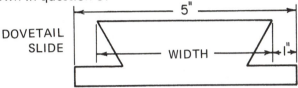

8. Find the lengths of A, B, C, and D. _____

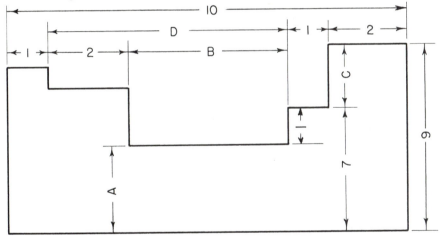

9. A gear on a splined shaft is shown. Four similar parts vary in _____
   dimensions, as shown in inches on the chart. Determine the width
   X of the gear on each of the four parts.

GEAR	A	B	C	D	X
1	2	6	3	16	
2	3	12	2	20	
3	4	17	4	28	
4	5	11	3	22	

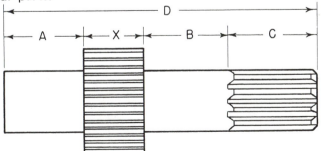

10. Five shafts with a total length of 109 inches are cut from one _____
    144-inch length of stock. How much is left?

Unit 3 MULTIPLICATION OF WHOLE NUMBERS

BASIC PRINCIPLES OF MULTIPLICATION

- Study unit 3 in *Basic Mathematics Simplified* for the principles of multiplication, as applied to whole numbers.

- Apply the principles of multiplication to the work of the machinist by solving the Review Problems which follow.

REVIEW PROBLEMS

1. What length of bar stock is required for 16 pieces of machine steel, if each piece is 2 inches long? _____

2. Twenty-three bolts, like the one shown, are to be made on a turret lathe. If a total of 5 inches for cut off and chucking is allowed, what minimum length of bar is needed? _____

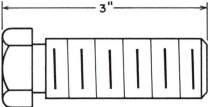

3. What length of bar is needed to cut 17 pins, each 2 inches long? (Allow a total waste of 2 inches for cutting.) _____

4. A stock clerk ordered the following steel bars: 7 bars, 1'' diameter x 11' long; 8 bars, 1 1/2'' diameter x 15' long; 17 bars, 2'' diameter x 19' long. What is the total number of feet of each size ordered? _____

5. A machine screw has 8 threads to the inch. How many threads are there in a threaded piece 7 inches long? _____

6. A job in a shop requires 3 hours of work on a lathe, 2 hours on a drill press, 5 hours on a shaper, and 7 hours on a milling machine. How many hours are required for each process if 235 similar jobs are ordered? _____

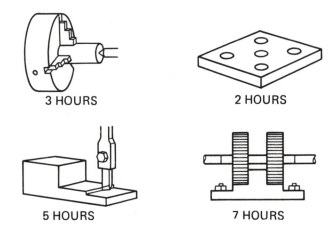

3 HOURS   2 HOURS

5 HOURS   7 HOURS

7. The manufacture of 200 tool blocks requires machining time in four departments, as follows: 20 hours planing, 30 hours milling, 50 hours grinding, 20 hours inspection. What is the total time required for 12 orders for 200 tool blocks?

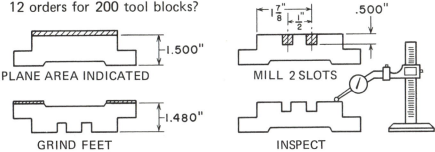

PLANE AREA INDICATED

MILL 2 SLOTS

GRIND FEET

INSPECT

8. A machinist used 456 bundles of 3/4-inch bar stock. Each bundle contained 27 bars. What is the total number of bars used?

9. A rough casting weighs 27 pounds. What is the total weight of 679 castings?

10. Each of 16 milling machines weighs 2478 lbs. What is the total weight of these machines?

11. Subtract 4735 from 7623 and then multiply the difference by 658. What is the product?

12. A firm buys 12 carloads of cast iron pigs, each carload weighing 116,000 pounds. What is the total weight?

13. A plant produces 2324 spindles on each shift. If the plant operates 2 shifts a day, 5 days a week, how many machine parts are produced in 4 weeks?

14. If the illustrated chisel requires 6 inches of 3/8-inch hexagonal steel, how long a piece is needed to make 9 chisels?

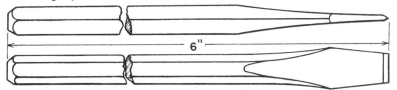

15. On a certain lathe, the stock turns 16 times for the tool to advance 1 inch. How many times must the stock revolve for the tool to travel 3 inches?

16. If it takes a machinist 2 hours to turn the part illustrated, how long does it take him to produce 17 more shafts?

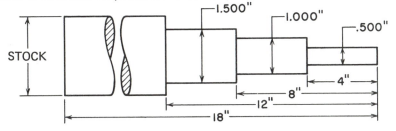

ST. PHILIPS COLLEGE LIBRARY

Unit 4 DIVISION OF WHOLE NUMBERS

BASIC PRINCIPLES OF DIVISION

- Study unit 4 in *Basic Mathematics Simplified* for the principles of division as applied to whole numbers.

- Apply the principles of division to the work of the machinist by solving the Review Problems which follow.

REVIEW PROBLEMS

1. A machinist has a piece of stock 256 inches long which he cuts into 8 equal pieces. How long is each piece? _____

2. A machine shop measures 162 feet in length with two aisles each 4 feet wide. As the diagram shows, there is a 2-foot space between one wall and the first machine. If each machine takes 9 feet with an additional 2-foot clearance, how many can be placed in line? _____

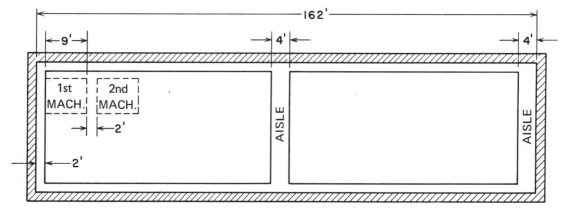

3. A machine shop owner spends $2375 to buy tools. Each tool cost an average of $16. How many tools did he buy? How much money is left? _____ _____

4. Determine the number of pieces that are machined per hour if 252,636 pieces are made in 12 hours. _____

5. How many pieces can be made from 240 bars of stock, each 216 inches long, if an automatic screw machine uses 4 inches with each cycle of operation? _____

6. Small ball bearings have to be wrapped at the rate of 26,400 in an 8-hour day. How many bearings must each of five girls wrap in a day? In an hour? _____ _____

7. An automatic screw machine uses 8 inches of stock, including cut off, to produce a part. How many complete parts can be machined from a 248-foot bar? (1 foot = 12 inches) _____

8. A punch press stamps out 4200 small discs per hour. How many hours does it take to produce 252,000 parts? _____

9. It takes a turret lathe operator 7 minutes to produce a part. How many parts does he produce in 8 hours? (1 hour = 60 minutes)

10. Four holes are drilled in the plate shown. The distance between holes is equal to the distance from the center of each end hole to the end of the plate. Find center distance X between holes.

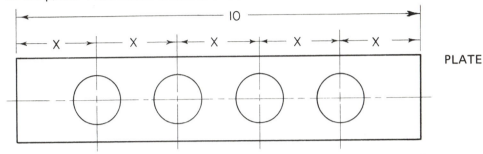

PLATE

11. How many pins like the one shown can be cut from a 4-foot bar of stock?

PIN

12. How many reamers like the one shown can be made from a piece of stock 3 feet long, allowing 1/8 inch for finishing both ends of each reamer?

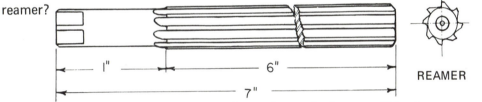

REAMER

13. How many reamers 7 inches in length can be made from an 8-foot bar, allowing 1/4 inch for cutting off and finishing both ends of each piece?

14. How many reamers 7 inches in length can be made from a 20-foot bar, allowing 3/16 inch waste on each for cutting off stock and finishing ends?

15. How many coiled springs can be made from a 42-pound bundle of wire if each spring weighs 3 ounces?

16. From a bar of steel 19 feet long, 72 bolts are made. One foot of stock is lost in cutting off and machining. What is the length of one bolt?

17. Four dozen twist drills cost $192. What is the cost per dozen? What does each drill cost?

18. A keg of bolts weighs 497 pounds. The average weight of each bolt (based on a sample of 7 bolts) is found to be 12 ounces. The keg weighs 11 pounds, when empty. How many bolts are in the keg? (1 pound = 16 ounces)

Unit 5 ADDITION OF FRACTIONS

BASIC PRINCIPLES OF ADDITION

- Study unit 7 in *Basic Mathematics Simplified* for the principles of addition as applied to fractions.

- Apply the principles of addition of fractions to the work of the machinist by solving the Review Problems which follow.

REVIEW PROBLEMS

1. When making a machine part, some material is wasted in such operations as facing, finishing the ends, and cutting the steel from the bar. If 1/8 inch is allowed for waste in making the shaft shown, what length of stock is required?

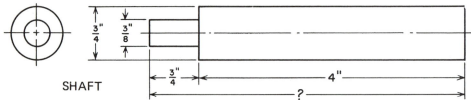

SHAFT

2. How long is the shaft, as illustrated? _____

3. If the small end of the shaft is changed to 1 1/8 inches long and all other dimensions remain the same, what is the overall length? _____

4. When the length dimensions are 5 1/2 inches and 15/16 inch, what is the overall length? _____

5. Allowing 1/8 inch for waste, how long a piece of steel is necessary for the shaft described in problem 4? _____

6. The length under the head of a bolt is the length from the under side of the head to the threaded end. In the bolt shown, it would be the length of the turned and threaded part or the length of the bolt without the head. Find the length under the head of the bolt. _____

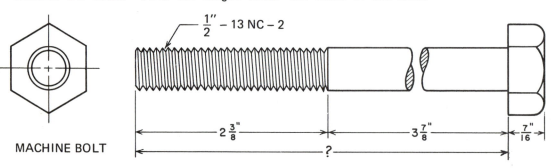

MACHINE BOLT

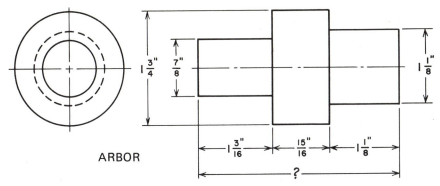

ARBOR

7. What is the overall length of the arbor as illustrated? _____

8. If 3/16 inch is allowed for waste, what length of stock is needed to make this arbor? _____

9. An arbor similar to the one shown has the end sections the same, but the center section is 1 7/16 inches long. What is the overall length? _____

10. What length of stock is needed to make an arbor like the one illustrated, if the linear dimensions are 17/32 inch, 13/16 inch, and 21/32 inch, and 1/8 inch is allowed for waste? _____

11. Five pieces of steel are cut from a bar. Their lengths are 7/8 inch, 9/16 inch, 3/4 inch, 27/32 inch, and 15/16 inch. Find the total length of the five pieces. _____

12. If 1/8 inch is wasted in making the cut for each of the pieces in problem 11, what is the total length of stock required for the five pieces? _____

13. Find the total length of the shaft as illustrated. _____

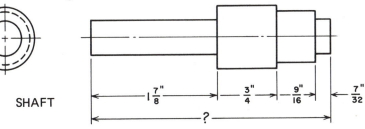

SHAFT

14. What length of stock will be used in making the illustrated link, if 1/8 inch is allowed for the cut off saw and finishing the ends? _____

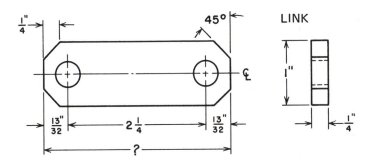

LINK

19

15. Five links are to be made like the one illustrated, with varying center distances between holes. Use the tabulated chart to find the length of stock for each size link.

Link Number	Centerline Distance "A" Between Holes	Overall Length "X"
1	1 53/64	
2	7 7/16	
3	1 13/64	
4	3 1/2	
5	2 15/16	

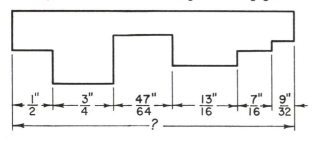

16. The time sheet for machining a part listed operations, as shown on the diagram. Find the total time for the machining.

TIME SHEET	
Manufacturing Operation	**Minutes**
Chucking on Lathe	2/3
Spotting and Drilling	2 2/5
Facing	1 1/2
Reaming	1/4
Total Time	

17. The sketch shows a profile gage that is used for checking work in a machine shop. The dimensions on the sketch are the lengths of the different steps. Find the overall length of the gage.

GAGE

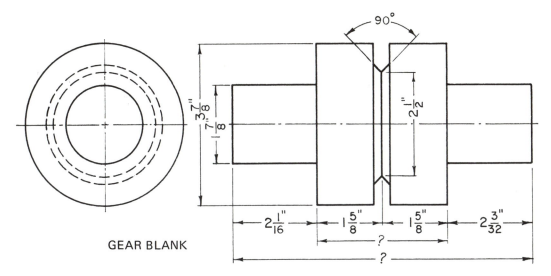

GEAR BLANK

18. Determine the missing dimensions on the illustrated gear blank. _____

19. If the linear dimensions of a gear blank like the one illustrated are 1 3/8 inches, 2 11/32 inches, 2 11/32 inches, and 1 57/64 inches, and 1/8 inch is allowed for waste, what is the length of stock needed for the job? _____

20. The time card, as illustrated, for a repair job shows the time spent on various machines. What is the total time charged to the job? _____

MAINTENANCE REPORT	
Name _____ **Job No.** 824	
Location of Repair	**Hours**
Engine Lathe	2 3/4
16-inch shaper	1 1/3
Radial drill press	5/6
Milling machine	2 1/4
Total Hours	

21. A plate has three holes spaced as illustrated. What is the center-to-center distance between the outside holes? What is the overall length of the plate? _____ _____

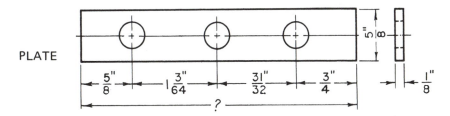

PLATE

22. What is the length of stock used, if 1/32 inch is allowed on each end for finishing? _____

Unit 6 SUBTRACTION OF FRACTIONS

BASIC PRINCIPLES OF SUBTRACTION

- Study unit 8 in *Basic Mathematics Simplified* for the principles of subtraction as applied to fractions.

- Apply the principles of subtraction of fractions to the work of the machinist by solving the Review Problems which follow.

REVIEW PROBLEMS

1. Find the diameter of the hole in the washer as illustrated. _____

2. What size hole will this washer have, if the wall thickness between hole and outer circumference is 13/32 inch? The outside diameter remains the same. _____

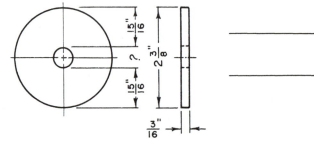

3. What is the diameter of the hole in the washer shown in the sketch? _____

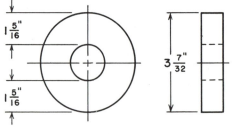

WASHER

4. What is the distance between the edge of the hole and the outside circumference of a 2 1/2-inch washer with a 1/2-inch hole? _____

5. Find the length under the head on the machine screw illustrated. _____

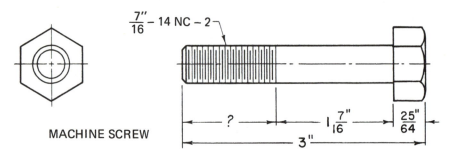

MACHINE SCREW

6. Find the length of threaded part on this machine screw. _____

7. If the distance between the head and threaded part is 1 5/16 inches and the length of thread and diameter of the machine screw remain the same, what is the overall length? _____

22

8. Find the width of the keyway in the motor shaft as illustrated.

9. What is the distance from the bottom of the keyway to the opposite side of the shaft?

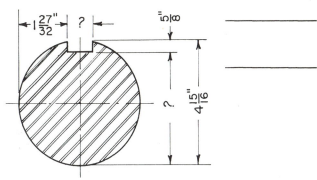

10. A keyway in a 2 1/4-inch shaft is milled to a depth of 5/16 inch, as illustrated. What is the measurement from the bottom of the keyway to the opposite side of the shaft?

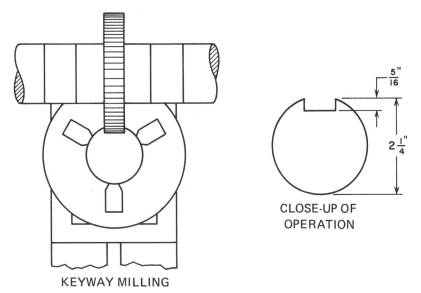

KEYWAY MILLING

CLOSE-UP OF OPERATION

11. A 2 1/2-inch shaft has a keyway 15/32 inch wide. What is the measurement from the side of the shaft to the edge of the keyway?

12. What is the missing dimension on the illustrated center punch?

CENTER PUNCH

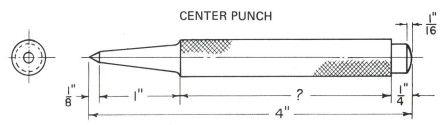

13. What is the missing dimension in problem 12, if the overall length is 4 23/32 inches and all other dimensions remain the same?

14. If two punches, one 4 1/64 inches and the other 4 3/32 inches overall, are made from a bar 9 7/16 inches long, what length of stock is wasted?

15. Find the inside diameter of the ring as illustrated.   _____

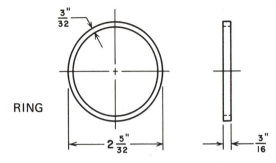

RING

16. Find the inside diameter of a ring, if the wall thickness is 1/16 inch and the outside diameter is 1 19/64 inches.   _____

17. If the outside diameter of a pipe measures 2 1/8 inches and the wall thickness is 9/32 inch, what is the inside diameter?   _____

18. If a 3/32-inch chip is cut from 1 1/4-inch diameter stock in a lathe, what is the finished diameter?   _____

19. A bar of cast iron 22 1/8 inches long has three pieces cut from it. They measure 6 1/2 inches, 4 7/8 inches, and 2 5/32 inches in length. If 1/8 inch is allowed for each saw cut, how long a piece of stock is left?   _____

20. A piece of cast iron 4 1/8 inches thick is planed to a thickness of 3 31/32 inches. What thickness of metal is removed?   _____

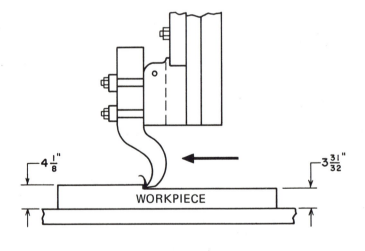

WORKPIECE

Unit 7 MULTIPLICATION OF FRACTIONS

BASIC PRINCIPLES OF MULTIPLICATION

- Study unit 9 in *Basic Mathematics Simplified* for the principles of multiplication as applied to fractions.

- Apply the principles of multiplication of fractions to the work of the machinist by solving the Review Problems which follow.

REVIEW PROBLEMS

1. If the chisel illustrated requires 5 7/8 inches of hexagonal steel, how long a bar is needed to make three chisels? _____

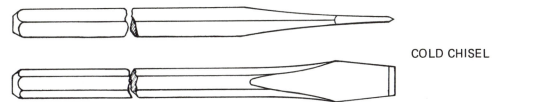

COLD CHISEL

2. What is the shortest bar that can be used for making five chisels, using 5 7/8 inches for each? _____

3. A chisel requires 4 9/16 inches of 1/2-inch hexagonal stock. How long a bar is needed to make twenty-five of these chisels? _____

4. What length of 1/2-inch hexagonal steel is used in making seventeen chisels, if each chisel requires 4 5/16 inches of stock? _____

5. What is the weight of 12 chisels, if each one weighs 1 3/4 pounds? _____

Note: The size of a nut is designated by the size of the tapped hole or the diameter of the thread on which it fits. A one inch hex. nut would have a hole tapped to fit a bolt one inch in diameter. Standards for other dimensions for each size of tapped hole are given in trade handbooks. Check the dimensions given for the nut as illustrated with the handbook and determine if it conforms to the American Standards for Bolts and Nuts. Note that standard nuts are the same length as the size of the tapped hole.

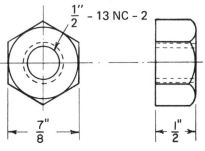

6. If 1/16 inch is allowed for waste on each nut, how long a piece of 13/16-inch hexagonal bar is needed to make a dozen 1/2-inch nuts? _____

7. If 3/32 inch is allowed for each nut, how much 1-inch hexagonal stock is needed for twenty-five 5/8-inch standard nuts? _____

8. With 3/32 inch allowed for waste for each nut, what length is left of a 1 1/8-inch hexagonal bar 20 feet long, after making fifty 3/4-inch nuts? _____

9. If 1/16 inch is allowed for finishing each end of a tap, what length _____
of stock is needed to make two taps such as the one illustrated?

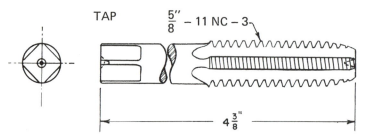

10. Under the same conditions what length of stock is needed for _____
1/2 dozen taps?

11. If the tool used to cut off the stock for this tap is 1/16 inch wide, _____
and 1/32 inch is allowed for finishing the ends, what length of stock
will be cut from a bar 10 feet long in making three taps?

12. With a 1/16-inch parting tool and 1/32 inch for finishing, what is the _____
shortest length bar that can be used in making 12 of these taps?

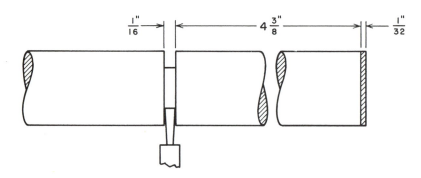

13. Under the same conditions, what length will be used for 36 taps cut _____
from a 16-foot bar?

14. At 87 1/2 cents each, how much do 12 taps cost? _____

15. A hacksaw blade has 14 teeth to the inch. The toothed section is _____
9 inches long. If a machinist uses only 4 1/4 inches of the toothed
section, how many teeth actually cut? How many teeth are not
being used?

16. If a hacksaw blade has 18 teeth per inch, how many teeth are cutting _____
when the workman uses a 3 3/8-inch stroke?

17. If the workman in the preceding problem lengthens his stroke to _____
7 1/8 inches, how many teeth are cutting?

Unit 8 DIVISION OF FRACTIONS

BASIC PRINCIPLES OF DIVISION

- Study unit 10 in *Basic Mathematics Simplified* for the principles of division as applied to fractions.

- Apply the principles of division of fractions to the work of the machinist by solving the Review Problems which follow.

REVIEW PROBLEMS

1. How many reamers like the one illustrated can be made from a piece of stock 3 feet long, if 1/8 inch is allowed on each reamer for waste? _____

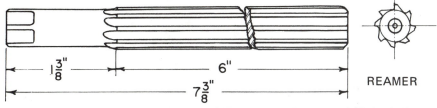

$1\frac{3}{8}"$ $6"$ REAMER

$7\frac{3}{8}"$

2. How many can be made from a 6-foot bar, allowing 1/8 inch for cutting off and 1/16 inch for finishing ends? _____

3. How many can be made from a 20-foot bar, allowing 3/16 inch of waste on each for cutting off stock and finishing ends? _____

4. How much stock is actually wasted in problem 3 (waste includes saw cuts, finishing ends, and bar ends not long enough for a reamer)? _____

5. If 1/16 inch of waste is allowed for each reamer, what length of bar stock is best to use — 18- or 20-foot length? _____

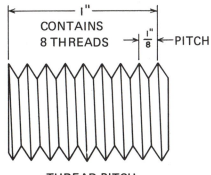

$1"$

CONTAINS
8 THREADS $\frac{1}{8}"$ ←PITCH

THREAD PITCH

Note: The pitch of a thread is the distance from a point on one thread to the corresponding point on the next and is usually expressed as a fraction. Machinists sometimes make the mistake of calling the number of threads in one inch the pitch. For example: A one-inch National Coarse (NC) thread has 8 threads to the inch. The pitch of this thread is 1/8 inch, but it is wrong to call it an 8 pitch thread.

6. A screw 4 inches long has 52 threads. How many threads per inch are there? What is the pitch? _____

7. Find the pitch and threads per inch on a screw 3 1/2 inches long with 56 threads.   _____

8. On a lathe job, the tool feeds 1/32 inch each time the stock turns once. How many times must the stock turn for the tool to advance 1 1/2 inches?   _____

9. How many times must the stock turn for the tool to advance 3 1/8 inches?   _____

10. If the feed is set for 3/64 inch per revolution, how many revolutions does the stock make while the tool is advancing 6 3/8 inches?   _____

11. A finishing tool on a shaper feeds 3/32 inch on each stroke. How many strokes does the ram make in finishing a surface 3 inches wide?   _____

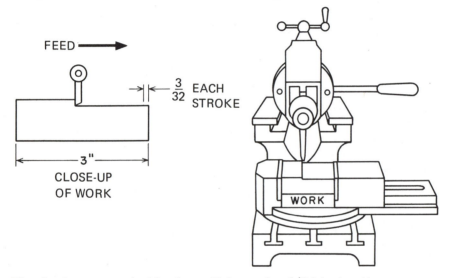

12. The feed on a vertical boring mill is set for 1/64 inch. How many revolutions does the work make while the tool is advancing 4 1/2 inches?   _____

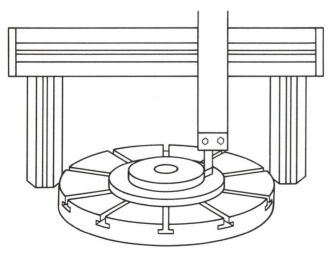

VERTICAL BORING MILL

13. A barrel of castings weighs 379 pounds. The empty barrel weighs _____
    15 pounds and one of the castings weighs 6 3/4 pounds. How many
    castings are in the barrel?

    Find the number of castings in each of the following:

Weight of barrel of castings	Weight of barrel	Weight of one casting	
14. 520 pounds	19 1/2 pounds	12 1/4 pounds	_____
15. 312 pounds	13 3/4 pounds	7/8 pound	_____
16. 417 pounds	20 pounds	8 1/8 pounds	_____
17. 561 3/4 pounds	16 1/2 pounds	22 1/2 pounds	_____
18. 863 pounds	22 pounds	1 3/4 pounds	_____

19. A bar of steel 22 feet 9 inches long is weighed and found to weigh _____
    107 11/16 pounds. What does it weigh per foot?

20. A steel bar 1 5/8 inches in diameter and 5 feet long weighs 35 1/4 _____
    pounds. Find the weight of a bar of the same diameter that is
    17 feet 9 1/2 inches long.

    Note: The circumference of a circle is equal to 3 1/7 times the
    diameter. The diameter, therefore, is equal to the circumference
    divided by 3 1/7.

    In the following problems give answers to the nearest 1/16 over:

21. The distance around a bar of steel is 2 1/2 inches; what is the diameter? _____

22. The circumference of a small gear blank is 5 1/2 inches. Find the _____
    diameter.

23. What is the diameter of a small bearing that has a circumference of _____
    7/8 inch?

24. A pulley rolls along a bench plate and travels 25 7/8 inches while _____
    making one complete turn. Find the diameter.

25. A ring has an outside circumference of 13 7/16 inches; what is its _____
    outside diameter?

26. If the stock from which the ring in the preceding problem is made _____
    is 3/8 inch thick, find the inside diameter and inside circumference _____
    of the ring.

27. A piece of brake lining 50 1/4 inches long is required to cover a _____
    friction feed roll. What is the diameter of the roll?

28. The windlass of a small hand hoist has 15 feet of rope wrapped _____
    around it in 5 turns. What is the diameter of the windlass?

29. What is the diameter of the largest pipe that can be rolled from a _____
    piece of sheet metal 48 inches wide if 3/4 inch is allowed for a joint?

Unit 9 MISCELLANEOUS FRACTIONS

BASIC PRINCIPLES OF FRACTIONS

- Review units 7 to 10 in *Basic Mathematics Simplified* for the principles which apply to the solution of fractions.

- Apply the principles for the solution of fractions to the work of the machinist by solving the Review Problems which follow.

REVIEW PROBLEMS

Allow 3/16 inch for cutting off stock and finishing ends in problems 1 to 5 inclusive.

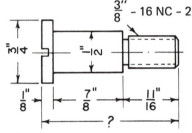

1. How many studs like the one illustrated can be made from a bar 1 foot 11 inches long? _____

2. How many can be cut from an 18-foot bar? _____

3. How many studs can be cut from 3 pieces which are 6 inches, 14 inches, and 3 feet long, respectively? _____

4. Two 3-foot pieces of 3/4-inch stock are available in the stock rack to make up an order of 100 studs. How many more 3-foot lengths are needed? _____

5. The stock rack contains 8 pieces, 1 foot 2 inches long; 6 pieces, 4 1/2 feet long; and 2 bars, 20 feet long. How much more stock must be ordered to fill an order for 600 studs? _____

6. If 1/16 inch waste is allowed on each, how long a piece of stock is required to make 3 punches of the same length as the one illustrated? _____

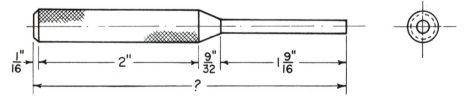

7. If 1/8 inch waste is allowed on each, what length of stock is needed to make 1/2 dozen punches? _____

8. If 3/16 inch waste is allowed on each, how many punches can be made from a piece of stock 2 feet long? _____

9. Allowing 1/8 inch waste on each, how many punches can be made from an 18-foot bar? _____

10. If one piece of stock 7 inches long, two pieces 12 inches long, and one piece 24 inches long are available, how many punches can be made, if 1/8 inch waste is allowed on each punch? _____

11. What length of stock is required to make the arbor as illustrated, if
    1/8 inch is allowed for cutting off the stock and finishing the ends?

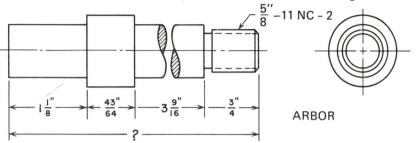

ARBOR

12. What length is necessary to make 3 arbors, allowing 1/8 inch on each
    for cut off and end finishing?

13. What length is sawed off a bar of stock for 10 arbors, if 3/16 inch is
    allowed on each for waste?

14. How many arbors can be cut from a piece of stock 3 feet 5 7/8 inches
    long, if 3/16 inch is allowed for cutting and squaring ends?

15. If 1/8 inch waste is allowed on each arbor, can 18- or 20-foot bars be
    cut with less waste?

16. A table in *Machinery's Handbook* lists the weight of hexagon steel
    bars 1 1/8 inch across the flats as 3 3/4 pounds per running foot.
    Using this constant, find the weight of a 1 1/8-inch hexagon steel bar
    that is 14 feet 7 inches long.

17. In the sketch, there are four holes
    equally spaced. Distance a is 17/32
    inch, and the distance b from each
    end to the center of the nearest
    hole is 3/4 of distance a.   Find
    the length of the piece.

18. A standard 1-inch pipe thread has 11 1/2 threads per inch. If a 1-inch
    pipe is screwed into a connection 6 5/8 turns, how far has the pipe
    entered into the connection?

19. If the pitch of a thread is 1/24 inch, what length of stock is needed
    for 38 threads?

20. What length of stock is needed for 102 threads of 1/24 inch?

21. How many threads are there on a bolt which has a threaded part
    3 1/2 inches with 1/18 inch pitch?

22. If there is a pitch of 1/14 inch, how many times does a nut revolve in
    moving 2 1/2 inches along a single thread? Note: The distance a nut
    or bolt moves in one revolution is called the "lead."

Unit 10 ADDITION OF DECIMALS

BASIC PRINCIPLES OF DECIMALS

- Study unit 13 in *Basic Mathematics Simplified* for the principles of addition as applied to decimals.

- Apply the principles of addition of decimals to the work of the machinist by solving the Review Problems which follow.

REVIEW PROBLEMS

1. What is the overall length of the gear shaft as illustrated? _____

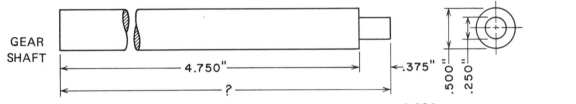

2. If the dimensions 4.750 inches and .375 inch are changed to 2.392 inches and 1.273 inches, what is the overall length of the shaft? _____

3. If the dimensions are 6.3125 inches and .5625 inch, what is the total length? _____

4. With dimensions 3.7454 inches and 1.9133 inches replacing the linear dimensions of the gear shaft shown in the sketch, what is the overall length to the nearest thousandth? _____

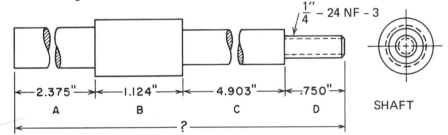

5. A threaded shaft is shown with a combination of diameter and thread belonging to a National Fine (NF) classification. What is the length without the threaded part? _____

Find the overall length of the shaft using the dimensions given for A, B, C, and D, to replace the linear dimensions shown in the sketch.

	A	B	C	D	
6.	3.137 inches	1.093 inches	5.001 inches	.625 inch	_____
7.	1.875 inches	.79055 inch	6.777 inches	1.3125 inches	_____

8. What is the total length of the template? _____

9. What is the total height? _____

10. What is the dimension "A"? _____

11. What is the dimension "B"? _____

12. What is the dimension "C"? _____

13. What is the dimension "D"? _____

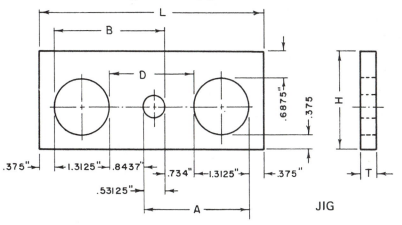

TEMPLATE

14. What is the overall length of the jig as illustrated? _____

JIG

15. One method of measuring between holes within close limits is to put accurately fitting plugs in the holes and to measure over or between the plugs with a micrometer or vernier caliper, as illustrated. Find the micrometer reading: across A, across B, across D.

_____
_____
_____

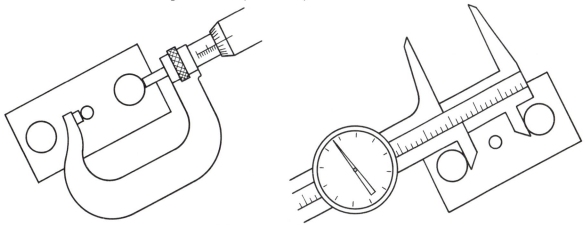

MEASURING ACROSS PLUGS WITH CALIPERS AND MICROMETER

16. What is the height of the jig? _____

Unit 11 SUBTRACTION OF DECIMALS

BASIC PRINCIPLES OF SUBTRACTION

- Study unit 14 in *Basic Mathematics Simplified* for the principles of subtraction as applied to decimals.

- Apply the principles of subtraction of decimals to the work of the machinist by solving the Review Problems which follow.

REVIEW PROBLEMS

1. What is the length of the hub on the worm gear shown? _____

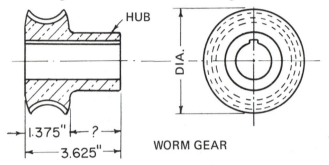

WORM GEAR

2. If the overall length is 4.500 inches and the hub length, 2.6875 inches, what is the hub thickness? _____

3. If the overall length is 4.25 inches and the gear thickness, 1.265 inches, what is the hub length? _____

4. The outside diameter of a collar is 1.375 inches and the inside diameter 1.103 inches. What is the wall thickness? _____

5. A collar has an outside diameter of 2.3145 inches and its inside diameter is .750 inch. What is the wall thickness? _____

If a piece changes in diameter or width at a constant rate for a part of its length, that part is called a taper. The total amount of taper (often called the total taper) is the difference in the diameters of the large and small ends of the taper.

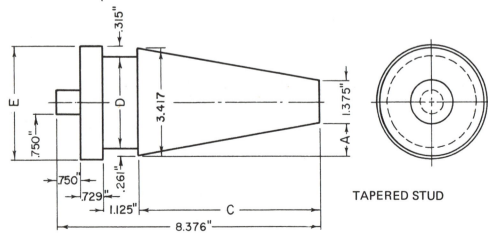

TAPERED STUD

6. What is the total taper of the tapered stud as illustrated? _____

7. What is the dimension C? _____

8. What is the diameter D? _____

9. What is the dimension E? _____

10. The outside diameter of a bushing is 2.419 inches and the wall thickness is .375 inch. What is the inside diameter? _____

11. A collar has an outside diameter of 1.9375 inches and a wall thickness of .427 inch. What is the inside diameter? _____

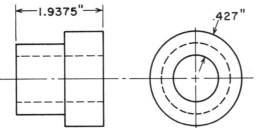

12. What is the inside diameter of a bushing that has an outside diameter of 2.418 inches and a wall thickness of .875 inch? _____

13. A lathe operator turns a .094 inch chip from a bar 3.952 inches in diameter. What is the finished diameter of the bar? _____

14. A bar is 2.750 inches before turning and 2.616 inches after. What is the depth of cut taken? _____

15. The gage drawing, shown below, is sent to a tool room for use in making the gage. The foreman finds that three important dimensions are missing. What are they? _____

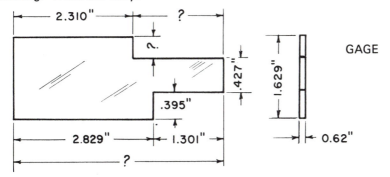

16. What is the resulting thickness after .126 inch is milled from each side of a plate which is 1.370 inches thick? _____

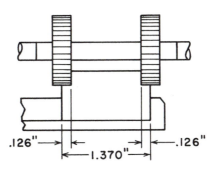

Unit 12 MULTIPLICATION OF DECIMALS

BASIC PRINCIPLES OF MULTIPLICATION

- Study unit 15 in *Basic Mathematics Simplified* for the principles of multiplication as applied to decimals.

- Apply the principles of multiplication of decimals to the work of the machinist by solving the Review Problems which follow.

REVIEW PROBLEMS

1. What length of stock is needed to make 5 pins, as illustrated, if .125 inch waste is allowed on each? _____

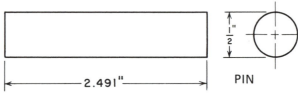

PIN

2. What length of stock is needed for 25 pins, if .093 inch waste is allowed on each? _____

3. If each pin weighs .1342 pound, what is the weight of 12 pins? _____

4. How much space will 3 of the illustrated thrust washers take up on a shaft? _____

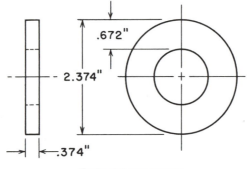

THRUST WASHER

5. How high is a stack of 13 of these washers? _____

6. How high is a stack of 25 washers, each of which is .425 inch thick? _____

7. How high is a stack of 64 washers, each of which is .287 inch thick? _____

8. What is the diameter of the hole in this washer? _____

   Note: To find the circumference of a circle multiply the diameter by 3.1416.

9. Diameter is 2.500 inches. Find the circumference. _____

10. Diameter is 1.904 inches. Find the circumference. _____

11. Diameter is 3.267 inches. Find the circumference. _____

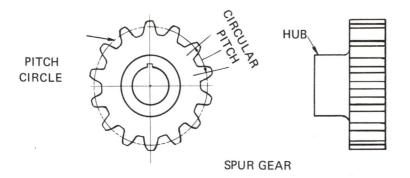

PITCH
CIRCLE

CIRCULAR
PITCH

HUB

SPUR GEAR

Note: The circular pitch of a gear is the distance along the pitch circle between corresponding points of adjacent teeth. To find the pitch circumference, multiply the circular pitch by the number of teeth.

12. Circular pitch .095 inch, number of teeth − 20.   _____

13. Circular pitch .287 inch, number of teeth − 42.   _____

14. Circular pitch 1.5904 inches, number of teeth − 125.   _____

15. Circular pitch .9382 inch, number of teeth − 51.   _____

16. What is the overall length of the illustrated roll with 9 of the   _____
     2 1/2-inch diameter sections?

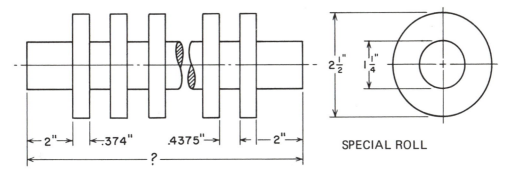

←2"→   ←.374"→   .4375"→   ←−2"→

?

$2\frac{1}{2}"$ $1\frac{1}{4}"$

SPECIAL ROLL

17. A roll similar to the one illustrated is built up with twenty-four   _____
     2 1/2-inch diameter sections.   Find the overall length.

18. A cast iron pulley contains 13.6 cubic inches of metal. What is the   _____
     weight of the pulley, if it weighs .26 pound per cubic inch?

Note: The distance across the corners of a square as illustrated is always equal to 1.414 times the length of one side of the square.

1.414" x SIDE

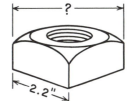

?

2.2"

19. What is the distance across the corners of a square nut which measures   _____
     2.2 inches on a side?

Unit 13 DIVISION OF DECIMALS

BASIC PRINCIPLES OF DIVISION

- Study unit 16 in *Basic Mathematics Simplified* for the principles of division as applied to decimals.

- Apply the principles of division of decimals to the work of the machinist by solving the Review Problems which follow.

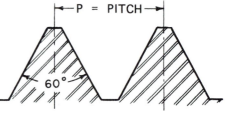

REVIEW PROBLEMS

Note: See any *Machinery's Handbook* for information on screw threads.

Find the pitch of each of the following threads to the nearest .001 of an inch.

1. 1/4-inch diameter, 28 threads per inch _____

2. 5/16-inch diameter, 24 threads per inch _____

3. 1/2-inch diameter, 20 threads per inch _____

4. 9/16-inch diameter, National Fine _____

National Coarse Thread (NC) formerly called U. S. Standard Thread.

P = Pitch
F = Width of Flat
$F = \dfrac{P}{8}$

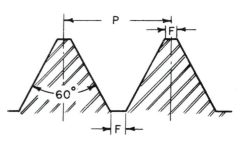

Note: Give answers to the following in ten thousandths (.0000).

Diameter	Threads per inch		
5. 1 inch	8	Find the width of the flat.	_____
6. 5/16 inch	18	Find the width of the flat.	_____
7. 2 inches	4 1/2	Find the width of the flat.	_____
8. 1/2 inch	National Coarse	Find the width of the flat.	_____

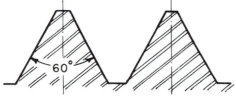

9. Pitch is .125   How many threads in 2 1/2 inches? _____

10. Pitch is .0625   How many threads in 1.875 inches? _____

11. Pitch is .05   How many threads in 12 3/4 inches? _____

12. Pitch is .03125   How many threads in 3 5/8 inches?

13. Cold rolled steel 1 inch in diameter weighs 2.68 pounds per foot of length. How many feet are there in a bundle of such bars weighing 203.5 pounds?   _____

14. A gallon of machine oil weighs 7.85 pounds. A tank partly filled with such oil weighs 128.5 pounds. If the tank itself weighs 16 pounds, how many gallons of oil are there in the tank?   _____

Note: In spur gears such as illustrated, the depth of the cut which forms the teeth of the gear is equal to 2.157 divided by the diametral pitch of the gear. This depth is expressed in inches and is usually carried out to the fourth decimal place.

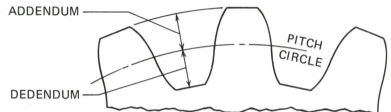

DEPTH OF TOOTH EQUALS ADDENDUM + DEDENDUM + CLEARANCE

15. According to the above rule, what is the depth of the teeth on a set of lathe gears which have a pitch of 16?   _____

16. What is the depth of the teeth on a gear of 12 pitch as used on a milling machine attachment?   _____

17. If .125 inch waste is allowed for each cut, how many of the illustrated bushings can be cut from a bronze bar 6 inches long, and what is the length of the piece left over?   _____

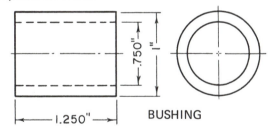

BUSHING

18. If there is .0625 inch waste on each piece, how many bushings can be cut from a piece 14 3/8 inches long; how long is the piece which is left?   _____
_____

The circumference of a pulley is equal to 3.1416 times the diameter. Therefore, the diameter is equal to the circumference divided by 3.1416 or π as it is usually indicated.

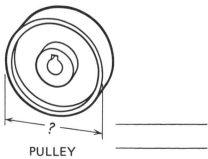

PULLEY

19. Circumference is 5.000 inches. What is the diameter?   _____

20. Circumference is 13.750 inches. What is the diameter?   _____

21. Circumference is 21.500 inches. What is the diameter?   _____

DECIMAL EQUIVALENTS OF FRACTIONS

Note: Any fraction may be changed to a decimal by dividing the numerator by the denominator.

1. Change the following fractions to decimals by this method:

   a. 5/8 _____   g. 23/64 _____

   b. 3/4 _____   h. 53/64 _____

   c. 7/16 _____   i. 19/32 _____

   d. 11/16 _____   j. 63/64 _____

   e. 31/32 _____   k. 27/32 _____

   f. 17/64 _____   l. 47/64 _____

2. Change the following fractions to decimals. Carry out to four places.

   a. 13/17 _____   d. 11/13 _____

   b. 7/9 _____   e. 3/5 _____

   c. 7/12 _____   f. 127/147 _____

Changing decimals to a common fraction.

Note: To change a decimal to the nearest number of 64ths, 32nds, 16ths, and so forth, multiply the decimal by the common fraction whose numerator and denominator are both equal to the denominator of the desired fraction.

3. Change the following decimals to the nearest indicated scale measurement and reduce to lowest terms:

   a. .7 inch to 32nds of an inch _____

   b. .31 inch to 64ths of an inch _____

   c. .566 inch to 16ths of an inch _____

   d. .86 inch to 32nds of an inch _____

   e. .809 inch to 16ths of an inch _____

Unit 14 MISCELLANEOUS DECIMALS

BASIC PRINCIPLES OF DECIMALS

- Study units 13 to 16 in *Basic Mathematics Simplified*.

- Apply the principles of decimals to the work of the machinist by solving the Review Problems which follow.

REVIEW PROBLEMS

1. What is the total length of the clevis as illustrated? _____

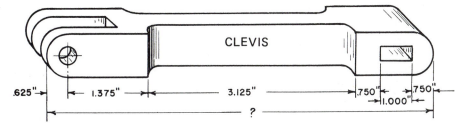

2. Three strips of brass with thicknesses of .086 inch, .035 inch, and .625 inch are placed on top of each other. What is the combined thickness of the strips? _____

3. Find the length and width of the profile gage as illustrated. _____

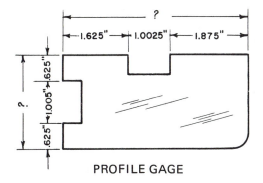

PROFILE GAGE

4. The steel tube illustrated does not have its outside diameter given. From the sketch shown, determine this diameter. _____

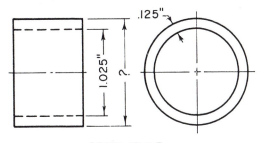

STEEL TUBE

5. The inside dimension of a gas pipe is .493 inch. The thickness of the metal is .091 inch. What is the outside diameter? _____

6. Using the drawing of the crank pin, determine the total length. _____

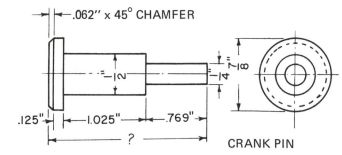

CRANK PIN

7. What is the total length of the pin as illustrated? _____

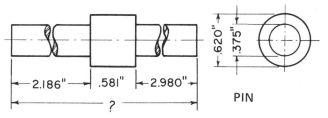

PIN

8. If the pin is enlarged 2.5 times, what are the dimensions? _____

9. A piece of 1 1/2-inch diameter machinery steel is turned down to a 1.037-inch diameter. How deep was the tool fed into the work by the lathe cross slide? _____

10. What is the length of the threaded part of the cap screw shown in the sketch? _____

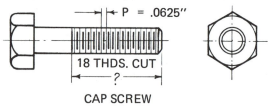

CAP SCREW

11. The hole in a sleeve is bored out for a 2-inch number 10 National Coarse thread. The thread depth is .065 inch. What is the diameter of the bored hole? _____

12. The minor diameter of a 1 1/2-inch number 6 National Coarse threaded bolt is 1.2835 inches. What is the thread depth, as shown in the drawing? _____

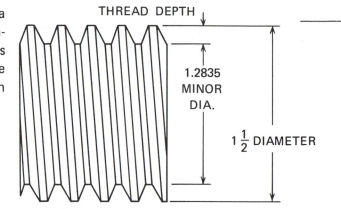

13. Number 10 copper wire measures 31.82 feet to the pound. How many pounds does a coil containing 125 feet of this wire weigh? _____

Unit 15 PERCENTAGE

BASIC PRINCIPLES OF PERCENTAGE

- Study units 25 and 26 in *Basic Mathematics Simplified* for the principles of simple percentage.

- Apply the principles of simple percentage to the work of the machinist by solving the Review Problems which follow.

REVIEW PROBLEMS

1. Express the following decimals as percents:

    a.   .85 _____   b.   .03 _____   c.   .15 _____   d.   .004_____   e.   .196 _____

2. Express the following percents as decimals:

    a.   20 percent   _____   d.   .2 percent   _____

    b.   98.9 percent   _____   e.   11 1/9 percent   _____

    c.   115 percent   _____

3. Express the following percents as common fractions:

    a.   40 percent   _____   c.   75 percent   _____

    b.   66 2/3 percent _____   d.   8 1/3 percent   _____

4. Express the following fractions as percents:

    a.   3/10 _____   b.   5/8 _____   c.   1/10 _____   d.   7/12 _____   e.   1/5 _____

5. Out of a lot of 60 castings, 5 percent are rejected because of defects.   _____
    How many are rejected?

6. If 3 1/3 percent of a lot of 60 castings are defective, how many are   _____
    rejected?

7. Of a lot of 72 castings, 12 1/2 percent are scrapped. How many   _____
    rejects does this represent?

8. An inspection of 96 castings revealed 16 2/3 percent to be defective.   _____
    How many failed to pass inspection?

9. Brazing metal is composed of 85 percent copper and 15 percent zinc.   _____
    How many pounds of copper are there in 25 pounds of brazing metal?

10. How many pounds of zinc are required for an alloy of 24 pounds of   _____
    brazing metal?

11. Naval brass is composed of 62 percent copper, 1 percent tin, and   _____
    37 percent zinc. How many pounds of copper are in 62 pounds of
    naval brass?

12. Find the number of pounds of tin in 62 pounds of naval brass. _____

13. What is the weight of zinc used in 57 pounds of naval brass? _____

14. If 6 2/3 pounds of naval brass are produced, how many pounds of zinc are required? _____

15. Clock brass consists of 64 1/4 percent copper, 34 percent zinc, and 1 3/4 percent lead. Find the number of pounds of each metal used in making 34 pounds of clock brass. _____ _____ _____

16. What is the weight of the zinc in 68 pounds of clock brass? _____

17. If 8 3/4 pounds of clock brass are prepared, find the number of pounds of each of lead, zinc, and copper that are required. _____ _____

18. What is the weight of the lead in 25 pounds of clock brass? _____

19. An alloy for soldering silver consists of 72 percent silver, 11 3/4 percent zinc, and the remainder, copper. Find the percent of copper in this alloy. _____

20. In transmitting an input of 80 horsepower by belts, 1.6 horsepower is lost by slippage. What percent is lost? _____

	Input in horsepower	Loss in horsepower	Percent of Loss
21.	27	8	
22.	125	2.56	
23.	51	3.45	
24.	11	1.1	
25.	43	1.09	

26. If turning 50 workpieces on a lathe results in 4 pieces being spoiled, what percent is scrapped? _____

	Number of workpieces	Number of spoiled pieces	Percent scrapped
27.	45	7	
28.	28	6	
29.	101	9	
30.	23	11	
31.	11	1	

32. A shop working 8 hours per day for 5 1/2 days per week changes to 9 hours per day for 5 days per week. Does the payroll increase or decrease? By what percent? _____

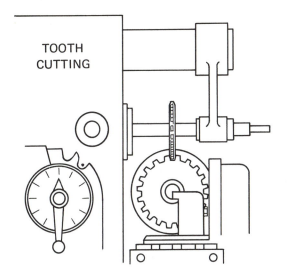

TOOTH
CUTTING

33. When a gear blank weighing 12 pounds is machined, 2 3/4 pounds of   _____
    the casting are removed. What percent of the metal is removed?

34. A finished gear weighing 6 3/4 pounds is cut from a gear blank weigh-   _____
    ing 9 5/8 pounds. What percent of the metal is removed?

35. In the preceding problem, what percent of the metal is left in the   _____
    gear?

36. A finished gear weighing 3.25 pounds is cut from a gear blank weigh-   _____
    ing 4.59 pounds. What percent of the gear blank weight is the weight
    of the finished gear?

37. What percent of metal is removed if the weights before and after   _____
    machining are 14 3/4 and 12.37 pounds, respectively?

38. Gear castings weigh 327 pounds; finished gears weigh 288 pounds.   _____
    What percent of the metal is removed in finishing?

The percent efficiency of a machine is found by dividing the
output by the input.

	Input in horsepower	Output in horsepower	Percent Efficiency
39.	5	4.750	
40.	7 1/2	7.35	
41.	21 1/2	22	

42. A 5 horsepower motor running at rated capacity is attached to   _____
    a machine which delivers 4.2 horsepower. What is the machine
    efficiency?

43. A machine requiring 48 horsepower is driven through belts from a   _____
    50 horsepower motor running at capacity. What is the efficiency of
    the belt drive?

44. In a certain lot of castings, 3 percent are unfit for use. If the rejected castings weigh 30 pounds, what is the total weight of the lot?   _____

	Percent Rejected	Weight Rejected	Total Weight
45.	6 1/2 percent	19 pounds	
46.	17 3/4 percent	37 pounds	

GEAR TRAIN

47. In a gear train, 4 percent of the power supplied is lost in friction. If the power loss is found to be 2 1/2 horsepower, what is the power supplied?   _____

48. What is the power delivered by the gear train in the preceding problem?   _____

49. The belt drive on a grinder has a loss of 2/3 horsepower with 97 percent efficiency. What is the power supplied?   _____

50. What is the power delivered at the grinding wheel?   _____

51. A drive through belts and countershafts is found to have 76 percent efficiency. If the loss is 2.314 horsepower, what power is delivered to the machine?   _____

52. A milling machine with 81 percent efficiency has a loss of 1.43 horsepower. What is the power delivered to the cutter?   _____

A certain type of bearing bronze is composed of 77 percent copper, 15 percent lead, and 8 percent tin.

53. If 13 pounds of copper are used, what is the weight of bronze made?   _____

54. What weight of bronze can be made, if 8 pounds of lead are used?   _____

55. The tin in a melting of the type of bearing bronze mentioned weighs 6 3/4 pounds. How much does the bronze weigh?   _____

56. Eleven and one-half pounds of lead are used in making bearing bronze for a certain job. How many pounds of bronze does the job require?   _____

57. Find the weight of bearing bronze in a melting and the weight of the lead and copper, if the melting contains 27 3/4 pounds of tin.   _____

58. How many pounds of lead and tin are used with 91.99 pounds of copper in making bearing bronze?   _____

Unit 16 LINEAR MEASURES

BASIC PRINCIPLES OF LINEAR MEASURE

- Study units 18 and 19 in *Basic Mathematics Simplified* for the principles of linear measure.

- Apply the principles of linear measure to the work of the machinist by solving the Review Problems which follow.

REVIEW PROBLEMS·

In the following problems, give answers to the nearest 1/64 inch. Unless otherwise specified, allow 1/16 inch for saw cut when called for.

1. Change the following lengths to inches.

    a.   3 feet _____   c.   1 foot 5 3/4 inches   _____

    b.   2 feet, 6 inches_____   d.   3 feet 4 7/16 inches   _____

2 Change the following lengths to feet and inches.

    a.   11.9 feet _____   c.   2.65 feet   _____

    b.   12.71 feet _____   d.   14.192 feet   _____

3. Express the following as a decimal in feet.

    a.   14 feet, 6 inches _____   b.   6 feet, 7 3/4 inches   _____

4. A piece 9 feet, 7 3/8 inches long is cut from a bar of 1 1/2-inch diameter machine steel which is 15 feet, 9 inches long. What length of bar is left?   _____

5. If 9 feet 9/16 inch is cut from a bar 20 feet long, what length remains?   _____

6. Find the length of the piece that remains if 3 feet, 7 15/16 inches are cut from a bar 12 feet, 2 3/32 inches long.   _____

7. Two pieces each 3 feet, 5 19/32 inches are cut from a piece of 3/4-inch diameter cold rolled steel 10 feet, 1 3/4 inches long. What length is left?   _____

8. A 20-foot bar of 3/4-inch hexagonal steel is cut into 3 equal parts. How long is each part?   _____

9. Four pieces each 3 feet, 2 1/2 inches long are cut from an 18-foot bar. What length is left?   _____

10. How many arbors each 1 foot, 9/16 inches long can be cut from a piece of 1 1/4-inch diameter stock which is 12 feet, 6 inches long?   _____

Unit 17 LIQUID MEASURE

BASIC PRINCIPLES OF LIQUID MEASURE

- Study unit 22 in *Basic Mathematics Simplified* for the principles of measurement as applied to liquid and time.

- Apply the principles of liquid and time measurements to the work of the machinist by solving the Review Problems which follow.

REVIEW PROBLEMS

1. If a machine uses 3 pints of oil a day, how many gallons will it use in 15 days? (1 quart = 2 pints; 1 gallon = 4 quarts) _____

2. What decimal part of a gallon is 7 pints? _____

3. If a machine shop uses 3 1/2 quarts of oil a week, how many weeks will 50 gallons of oil last? _____

4. A tank holding 350 gallons has two pipes connected to it; one empties out 2 quarts in 5 seconds, and the other, 17 gallons per minute. How long will it take to empty the tank with both pipes flowing? _____

5. If oil costs $27.50 for a 50-gallon drum, with $1.00 rebate when the drum is returned, what must the selling price be per quart in order to make 15 percent profit? _____

6. How many minutes in 5 3/4 hours? (60 minutes = 1 hour) _____

7. A machinist works from 8:20 in the morning until 10 minutes before noon. At $3.00 per hour, how much does he earn? _____

8. A man starts work in the morning and works from 7:25 until 11:10. What is his pay for this time, at $1.75 per hour? _____

9. To turn a certain piece of work requires 3 hours 40 minutes. What time is needed for turning 25 pieces? _____

10. A job requires 6 hours 25 minutes turning, 45 minutes drilling, and 1 1/2 hours on the shaper. What is the total job time? _____

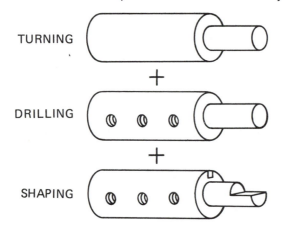

TURNING

+

DRILLING

+

SHAPING

Unit 18 HORSEPOWER

BASIC PRINCIPLES OF MEASUREMENT

- Study units 63 and 66 in *Basic Mathematics Simplified* for the principles of measurement as applied to horsepower problems.

- Apply the principles for measuring horsepower to the work of the machinist by solving the Review Problems which follow.

REVIEW PROBLEMS

One horsepower is equal to 33,000 foot-pounds per minute.

1. A planer weighing 99,000 pounds is raised 1 foot in one minute. What horsepower is used? _____

2. It takes one minute to raise a 66,000-pound boring mill 6 feet. What horsepower is used? _____

3. What horsepower is used if a machine weighing 16,500 pounds is raised 10 feet in 7 minutes? _____

4. A 1-ton casting is raised 22 feet in one minute. Find the horsepower required. _____

5. It takes 3/4 minute for a hoist to raise a 1,842-pound girder 122 feet. Find the horsepower of the engine. _____

6. What is the rating of a 5-horsepower motor in watts? _____

7. How many watts are consumed by a motor running under a 12-horsepower load? _____

8. A wattmeter in the line shows that a motor is drawing 2238 watts. What horsepower is being delivered if it is assumed there are no losses? _____

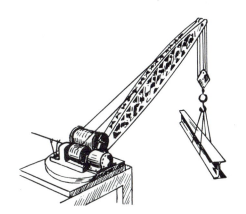

Unit 19 METRIC SYSTEM

BASIC PRINCIPLES OF METRIC SYSTEM

- Study unit 23 in *Basic Mathematics Simplified* for the principles of measurement as applied to the metric system.

- Apply the principles of the metric system of measurement to the work of the machinist by solving the Review Problems which follow.

REVIEW PROBLEMS

Refer to the metric tables in *Basic Mathematics Simplified*.

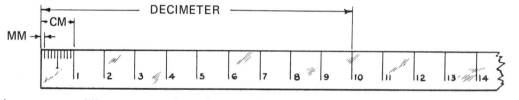

1. How many millimeters are there in one decimeter? _____
2. How many millimeters are there in one meter? _____
3. How many centimeters are there in one meter? _____
4. How many millimeters are there in 7 decimeters? _____
5. How many millimeters are there in 85 centimeters? _____

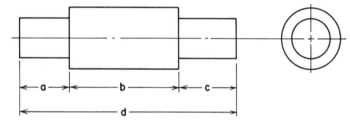

In the preceding sketch

6. a = 35 millimeters, b = 110 millimeters, c = 45 millimeters Find d. _____

7. d = 45 centimeters, a = 75 millimeters, b = 150 millimeters Find c. _____

8. d = 3 decimeters, a = 81 millimeters, c = 93 millimeters Find b. _____

In the accompanying sketch

9. a = 95 millimeters, b = 45 millimeters Find c. _____

10. a = 9 centimeters, b = 38 millimeters Find c. _____

11. a = 1 decimeter, b = 7 centimeters Find c. _____

12. a = 2 decimeters, c = 35 millimeters Find b. _____

13. b = 6 centimeters, c = 22 millimeters Find a. _____

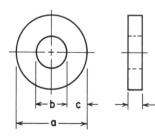

14. How many pieces of 3/16-inch drill rod, each 37 millimeters long, can be cut from a bar 1 meter long, if 1.5 millimeters is allowed for each cut? _____

Unit 20 METRIC EQUIVALENTS

BASIC PRINCIPLES OF METRIC EQUIVALENTS

- Review unit 23 and study table II in *Basic Mathematics Simplified* for the principles of measurement as applied to metric equivalents.

- Apply the principles of metric equivalents to the work of the machinist by solving the Review Problems which follow.

REVIEW PROBLEMS

1 meter = 39.37 inches   1 inch = 25.4 millimeters

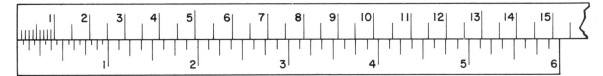

CENTIMETERS

INCHES

1. How many inches are there in one decimeter?   _____

2. How many inches are there in 6 centimeters?   _____

3. How many inches are there in 37 millimeters?   _____

4. What is the length in millimeters of a 6-inch rule?   _____

5. What is the length in centimeters of a yardstick?   _____

6. Find the length in decimeters of a 12-foot planer table.   _____

7. Does a wrench with an opening of 25 millimeters fit a nut which   _____
    measures 1 inch across the flats?

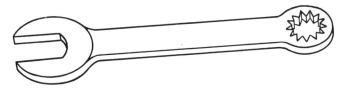

8. What is the diameter in millimeters of a pulley 18 inches in diameter?   _____

9. What is the equivalent of 3 feet, 3 3/4 inches in millimeters?   _____

10. How many pieces 1 meter long can be cut from a 20-foot steel bar?   _____

11. How many reamer blanks, each 20 centimeters long, can be cut from   _____
    a bar 6 feet long? Allow 3 millimeters for each saw cut.

12. A ten-foot bar of 5/8-inch diameter mild steel is divided into 8 equal   _____
    parts. Give the length of each part in millimeters.

13. Number 16-gage sheet steel is 1/16 inch thick. Find its thickness in   _____
    millimeters (to 4 decimal places).

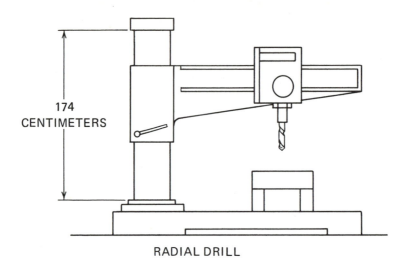

RADIAL DRILL

14. The column of a radial drill is 174 centimeters high. What is its height in feet, inches, and fractions of an inch? _____

15. A steel bar is 5 feet, 11 1/2 inches long. What is its length in centimeters? _____

16. Eight pieces of stock each 18 centimeters long with 1 centimeter waste each are cut from a 20-foot bar. What length is left in feet and inches? _____

17. If 7 pieces of stock 75 millimeters long with 3 millimeters waste are cut from an 18-foot bar, what length is left in feet and inches? _____

18. Find the difference in total length between 3 pieces of stock, 375 millimeters long and 2 pieces, 5 7/8 inches long. _____

19. Find the difference between 5 decimeters and 18 inches. _____

20. An order is received for 215 pins each 47 centimeters long to be turned from 1/4-inch round steel. If 1/8 inch is allowed for waste on each piece, what length of stock is required? _____

21. A piece of work must be turned to a diameter of 43 centimeters. If 1/16-inch excess diameter is allowed for turning, what is the smallest diameter stock that can be used? (The stock on hand is in sixteenths.) _____

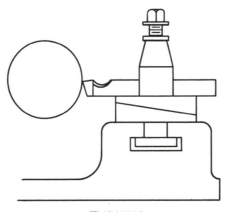

TURNING

Unit 21 ANGULAR MEASUREMENT

BASIC PRINCIPLES OF ANGULAR MEASUREMENT

- Study unit 20 in *Basic Mathematics Simplified* for the principles of angular measurement.
- Apply the principles of angular measurement to the work of the machinist by solving the Review Problems which follow.

REVIEW PROBLEMS

1. How many degrees are there in a right angle? _____

2. How many degrees are there in 2 right angles? _____

3. How many degrees are there in 3 right angles? _____

4. How many 60 degree angles are there in 2 right angles? _____

5. How many 30 degree angles are there in 3 right angles? _____

6. How many 45 degree angles are there at the center of a circle? _____

Complementary and supplementary angles

Angle A plus angle B = 90 degrees

Angle A is the complement of angle B

Angle B is the complement of angle A

Angle A plus angle C = 180 degrees

Angle A is the supplement of angle C

Angle C is the supplement of angle A

7. Angle A = 30 degrees. Give value of angle B. _____

8. Angle A = 30 degrees. Give value of angle C. _____

9. Angle A = 61 degrees 40 minutes. Give value of angle B. _____

10. Find the complement of 22 degrees 47 minutes. _____

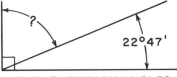

COMPLEMENTARY ANGLES

11. Find the supplement of 105 degrees 22 minutes. _____

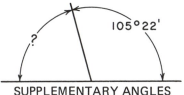

SUPPLEMENTARY ANGLES

12. Find the angle whose complement is 22 degrees 30 minutes. _____

Angle A = 30 degrees

Angle B = 20 degrees

Angle D = 65 degrees 22 minutes

Angle F = 118 degrees 40 minutes

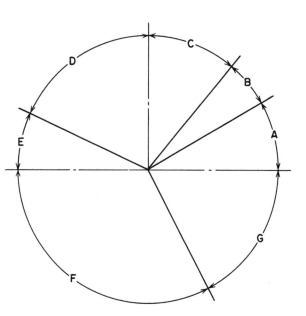

Using the information and the diagram given, find the values in problems 13-18.

13. What is the sum of angles A and B? _____

14. Find value of angle C if A, B, and C total 90 degrees. _____

15. What is the sum of angles A, B, C, and D? _____

16. Find the value of angle E. _____

17. What is the sum of angles A, B, C, D, E, and F? _____

18. Find angle G. _____

19. If the included angle R (see diagram) is 48 degrees, what is the angle on one side of the centerline? _____

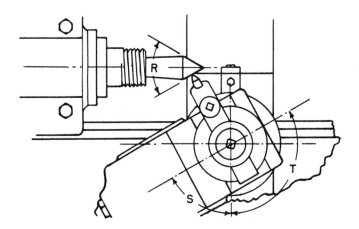

20. How many degrees is a compound rest swiveled on a lathe to cut an included angle of 20 degrees?   _____

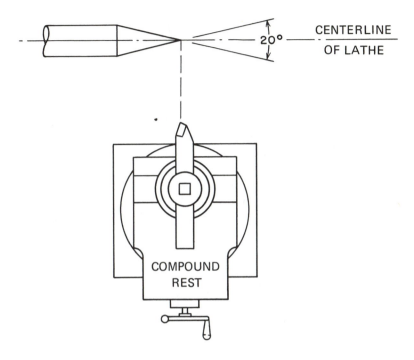

21. If angle R equals 26 degrees, how many degrees are there in angle S?   _____

22. If the included angle R is 45 degrees, how many degrees are there in angle T?   _____

23. How many degrees do you move the compound rest on a lathe to cut an included angle of 72 degrees 30 minutes?   _____

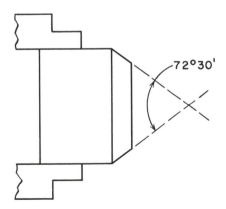

24. What is the value of angle S in the preceding problems?   _____

Unit 22 POWERS AND ROOTS

BASIC PRINCIPLES OF POWERS

- Study units 55, 56, and 57 in *Basic Mathematics Simplified* for the principles of powers.

- Apply the principles of powers to the work of the machinist by solving the Review Problems which follow.

REVIEW PROBLEMS

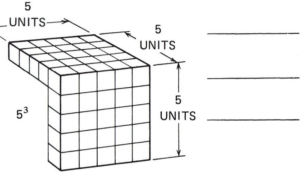

1. a. Find the value of 6 squared, usually written 6^2. _____

   b. Raise 5 to the third power (or 5^3). _____

   c. What is the third power of 17 (or 17^3)? _____

2. a. What is the cube of 15.3 (or 15.3^3)? _____

   b. If 123 is taken as a factor 3 times (123^3), what is the result? _____

3. Find the values of the following expressions:

   a. $.07^2$ (This could be read, point 0 seven squared.) _____

   b. .193 raised to the third power. _____

4. You have noticed by this time that there are a number of different ways of reading a mathematical expression consisting of a number and its exponent. In the following, write out the expression before performing the operation:

   a. 3.1^4 _____ b. 1.093^2 _____ c. 1.07^5 _____

5. a. Find the square of 2/3, or $(2/3)^2$. _____

   b. What is the value of 3/4 squared, or $(3/4)^2$? _____

   c. What is the cube of 7/8, or $(7/8)^3$? _____

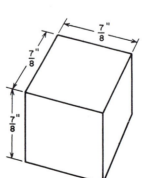

Unit 23 SQUARE ROOT

BASIC PRINCIPLES OF SQUARE ROOT

- Study units 59 to 61 in *Basic Mathematics Simplified* for the principles of square root.

- Apply the principles of square root to the work of the machinist by solving the Review Problems which follow.

REVIEW PROBLEMS

1. Write the answers to the following:

   a. $\sqrt{4}$ _____   b. $\sqrt{25}$ _____   c. $\sqrt{64}$ _____

   Note: The square root of a number may be indicated in either of two ways: $\sqrt{4}$ or $4^{1/2}$.

   $4^{1/2}$ ⟵──── ROOT OF THE NUMBER
   ┌──── POWER OF THE NUMBER

   INDICATES SQUARE ROOT

2. Find the values of the following expressions:

   a. $\sqrt{144}$ _____   d. $\sqrt{53361}$ _____

   b. $\sqrt{225}$ _____   e. $\sqrt{516961}$ _____

   c. $\sqrt{625}$ _____

3. Find the square root of

   a. 23804641 _____   b. 120409 _____   c. .0064 _____

4. Find the square root of 2, correct to four decimal places. _____

5. Find the answers to each of the following, correct to four decimal places.

   a. $\sqrt{143}$ _____   d. $\sqrt{287}$ _____

   b. $\sqrt{287}$ _____   e. $\sqrt{20.7846}$ _____

   c. $\sqrt{7^{1/2}}$ _____

6. Find the square root of the fraction 4/25. _____

   Note: To find the square root of a common fraction when the numerator and denominator are perfect squares, find the square root of the numerator and the square root of the denominator.

   $$\sqrt{4/25} = \sqrt{4}/\sqrt{25} = 2/5$$

7. What is the value of $(49/169)^{1/2}$? _____

8. Find the square root of 7/9, correct to five decimal places. _____

Unit 24 REVIEW OF POWERS AND ROOTS

REVIEW OF BASIC PRINCIPLES

- Study units 55 to 57 and 59 to 61 in *Basic Mathematics Simplified* for the principles of powers and roots for the solution of practical problems.

- Apply the principles of powers and roots to the work of the machinist by solving the Review Problems which follow.

REVIEW PROBLEMS

Note: The area of a square is equal to the square of one of its sides. The side of a square equals the square root of its area.

1. Find the sides of a square whose area is .5625 square inches. _____

Note: The area of a circle is equal to 3.1416 times the square of its radius. The radius of a circle equals the square root of the area after it has been divided by 3.1416.

2. If a square has an area of 5.125 square inches, find the sides and the distance around it (the perimeter). _____

3. Find the area of a circle whose radius is 2.375 inches. _____

4. a. If the radius of a circle is 6 3/4 inches, what is the area? _____

    b. Find the area of circles whose radii are .0193 inch and 3.912 inches, respectively. _____

5. The areas of three circles are 12.5664 square inches, 3 square inches, and 4 square inches, respectively. Find the radius of each of the three circles. _____ _____ _____

6. A circle has a radius of 6.39 inches. Find its area. _____

7. The area of a circle is 27.15 square inches. Find its diameter. (The diameter is equal to twice the radius.) _____

8. The side of a square is 6.91 inches. Find its area. _____

9. Find the side of a square whose area is 32.9 square inches. _____

Note: The area of a sphere is equal to $3.1416D^2$, or the diameter squared times 3.1416. To find the diameter of a sphere when the area is given, proceed as in finding the radius of a circle.

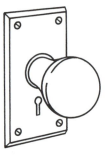

10. Find the diameter of a brass door knob which has an area of 53.456 square inches. _____

11. A square piece of sheet metal has an area of 132,651 square inches. How long is one side? _____

12. A square building covers an area of 961 square feet. Find the length of each side of the building. _____

13. A circle has an area of 637.94 square inches. Find its diameter to the nearest tenth of an inch. $D = \sqrt{A/.7854}$ _____

Unit 25 TRIANGLES

REVIEW OF BASIC TRIANGLES

- Review units 55 to 57 and 59 to 61 in *Basic Mathematics Simplified* for the principles of powers and roots as applied to triangles.

- Apply the principles of powers and roots to the work of the machinist by solving the Review Problems which follow.

REVIEW PROBLEMS

1. On the illustrated template, find the distance from the center of hole A to the nearest corner. _____

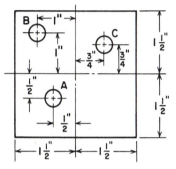

2. What is the measurement from the center of hole B to the nearest corner? _____

3. How far is it from the center of hole C to the nearest corner? _____

4. How long is the diagonal of a square bar 2 inches on a side? _____

5. Find the length of a side of the largest square section that can be milled from a round bar 2 inches in diameter. _____

6. A piece of flat stock 3 inches wide has a diagonal of 3.354 inches. What is the thickness of the stock? _____

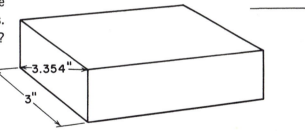

7. A block of steel, rectangular in section, and 1 inch in thickness, is milled from a piece of round stock. What is the greatest width obtainable, if the stock is 2 inches in diameter? _____

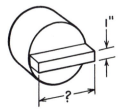

SECTION 7 — RATIO AND PROPORTION

Unit 26 RATIO AND PROPORTION

BASIC PRINCIPLES OF RATIO

- Study unit 51 in *Basic Mathematics Simplified* for the principles of ratio.
- Apply the principles of ratio to the work of the machinist by solving the Review Problems which follow.

REVIEW PROBLEMS

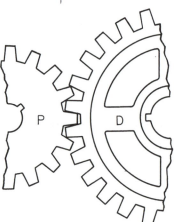

1. If gear A has 80 teeth and gear B has 40 teeth, what is the ratio of A to B? What is the ratio of B to A?   _____

2. Two gears, A and B, are working together. A has 60 teeth and B has 20, what is the ratio of A to B? What is the ratio of B to A?   _____

3. Two gears, as illustrated, have a ratio of 3 to 1. If the larger of the two gears, D, has 33 teeth, how many teeth are there in gear P?   _____

4. If the two gears shown in the preceding diagram each have 48 teeth, what is the ratio of P to D?   _____

5. Two gears in mesh have a ratio of 5 to 4. If the larger of the two gears has 60 teeth, how many teeth are there in the other gear?   _____

6. In a belt drive like the one shown, pulley A is 20 inches in diameter; and B, 10 inches. What is the ratio of the diameter of A to the diameter of B?   _____

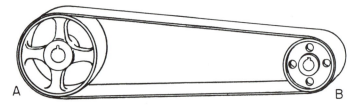

7. How many times does pulley A turn while pulley B turns once?   _____

8. How many times does pulley B turn while pulley A turns once?   _____

Unit 27 SIMILAR TRIANGLES

BASIC PRINCIPLES OF SIMILAR TRIANGLES

- Study units 52 and 53 in *Basic Mathematics Simplified* for the principles of ratio and proportion as applied to similar triangles.

- Apply the principles of ratio and proportion to the work of the machinist by solving the Review Problems which follow.

REVIEW PROBLEMS

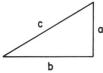

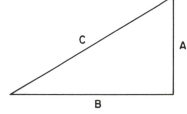

The sides of similar triangles are in proportion as follows:

$$a:A = b:B \quad \text{or} \quad a:A = c:C \quad \text{or} \quad b:B = c:C$$

1. a = 6   b = 8   A = 20   Find B.   _____

2. a = 6   c = 10   A = 20   Find C.   _____

3. a = 7   b = 3   c = 9   A = 11   Find C.   _____

4. Find B using values given in problem 3.   _____

5. A = 27   B = 12   C = 19   b = 5   Find a.   _____

6. Find c using values given in problem 5.   _____

7. The piece illustrated tapers as indicated. Find the amount of taper   _____
    in a piece 13 inches long.

    Note: The proportion may be formed in either of two ways.

    $$12:13 = 8:x \quad \text{or} \quad \frac{12}{13} = \frac{8}{x}$$

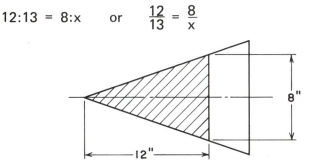

8. Find the taper on a gage 11 inches long which has a taper of 3 1/4   _____
    inches per foot.

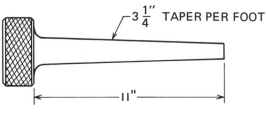

TAPERED GAGE

Unit 28 MISCELLANEOUS PROBLEMS

REVIEW OF BASIC PRINCIPLES

- Review units 51 to 53 in *Basic Mathematics Simplified* for the principles of ratio and proportion.

- Apply the principles of ratio and proportion to the work of the machinist by solving the Review Problems which follow.

REVIEW PROBLEMS

1. How much would the illustrated piece taper in 2 inches?　　　　　　　　_____

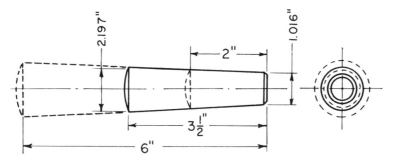

2. How much does this piece taper, if it is 6 inches long?　　　　　　　　_____

3. Find the taper per foot of the piece illustrated.　　　　　　　　_____

4. A piece 17 inches long tapers .015 inch. How much is the taper in　　_____
   4 1/2 inches of length?

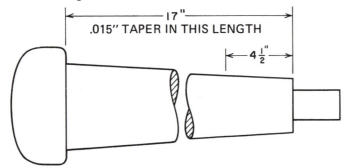

.015" TAPER IN THIS LENGTH

5. A piece tapers .796 inch in 2 1/2 inches of length. What length must　　_____
   the piece be to taper 1 inch?

6. The taper of a piece is 1/2 inch per foot. What is the length of the　　_____
   piece when the taper is .0359 inch?

7. If four pieces can be milled in 7 hours, how long will it take to mill　　_____
   21 pieces?

8. A square bar of steel 46 inches long weighs 41.995 pounds. What is　　_____
   the weight of a piece of the same bar 31 5/8 inches long?

9. If 85 holes can be tapped in 2 1/2 hours, how many hours does it take　　_____
   to tap 1500 holes?

Unit 29 GEAR RATIOS

REVIEW OF BASIC PRINCIPLES

- Review units 51 to 53 in *Basic Mathematics Simplified* for the principles of ratio and proportion as applied to gear ratios.

- Apply the principles of ratio and proportion to the work of the machinist by solving the Review Problems which follow.

REVIEW PROBLEMS

1. A gear having 80 teeth turns 150 revolutions per minute driving a 40-tooth gear. Form a proportion and solve to find revolutions per minute of the driven gear. _____

2. A 96-tooth gear is meshed with a gear having 40 teeth. If the large gear revolves 65 turns per minute, how many turns does the small gear make? _____

3. A 38-tooth gear running 360 revolutions per minute drives another gear at 190 revolutions per minute. How many teeth does the second gear have? _____

4. Two gears have a speed ratio of 4.6 to 1. If the smaller gear has 15 teeth, what is the number of teeth on the larger gear? _____

5. Two shafts 18 inches on centers are connected by gears so that one turns twice as fast as the other. What is the pitch diameter of each gear that is used? _____

   Note: The gear which drives another gear is usually referred to as the pinion.

	Teeth		Revolutions Per Minute	
	Pinion	Driven Gear	Pinion	Driven Gear
6.	60	15	110	_____
7.	90	_____	250	100
8.	_____	120	64	48

9. A gear having 3 1/2-inch pitch diameter with a speed of 210 revolutions per minute drives a gear having 5 1/4-inch pitch diameter. What is the speed of the second gear? _____

10. If an idler gear of 4 1/2 pitch diameter is placed between the last two gears in the preceding problem, what is the speed of the last gear? Does the last gear turn in the same direction as before the idler was introduced? Does the size of the idler affect the speed of the driven gear? _____ _____ _____

11. A gear of 44 teeth turning 128 revolutions per minute drives a 37-tooth gear. What are the revolutions per minute of the second gear? _____

12. What size gear is used to achieve 250 revolutions per minute, if the pinion has 20 teeth and turns 100 revolutions per minute? _____

Unit 30 PULLEY SPEEDS

REVIEW OF BASIC PRINCIPLES

- Review units 51 to 53 in *Basic Mathematics Simplified* for the principles of ratio and proportion as applied to pulley speeds.

- Apply the principles of ratio and proportion to the work of the machinist by solving the Review Problems which follow.

REVIEW PROBLEMS

1. The diameters of two pulleys connected by a belt are 24 inches and 18 inches. If the larger pulley turns 245 revolutions per minute, what is the speed of the smaller pulley? _____

2. What size standard pulley (see handbook) should be placed on a countershaft to turn 408 revolutions per minute, if it is to be driven by a 14-inch pulley on a line shaft turning 175 revolutions per minute? _____

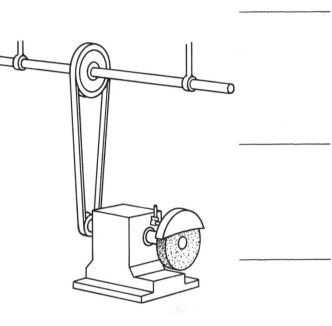

3. What size pulley should be placed on a countershaft turning 150 revolutions per minute to drive a grinder with a 4-inch pulley which is to turn 1200 revolutions per minute? _____

4. What size pulley would replace the 32-inch pulley in the preceding problem, if a line shaft speed of 200 revolutions per minute is desired? _____

5. A 14-inch emery wheel is to have a surface speed of 5500 feet per minute. What size pulley will be used on the line which turns 220 revolutions per minute to drive the 5-inch pulley on the grinder shaft? _____

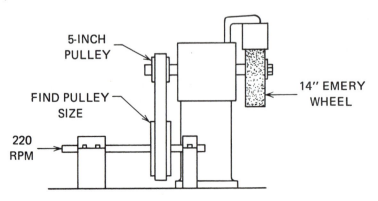

5-INCH PULLEY

FIND PULLEY SIZE

220 RPM

14″ EMERY WHEEL

6. If, in the diagram, A is 16 inches and turns 220 revolutions per minute, B is 6 inches, and C is 24 inches, what size pulley must be placed at D to obtain 1760 revolutions per minute?

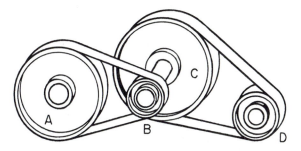

7. B is 30 inches in diameter; C, 45 inches; D, 18 inches. Find the diameter of A if the speed of A is 420 revolutions per minute and the speed D is 380 revolutions per minute.

8. A is 11 inches in diameter; B, 36 inches; D, 20 inches. Find the diameter of C if the speed of A is 840 revolutions per minute and the speed of D is 700 revolutions per minute.

9. A is 22 inches in diameter; C, 35 inches; D, 24 inches. Find the diameter of B if the speed of A is 200 revolutions per minute and of D is 200 revolutions per minute.

10. Pulley A, 8 inches in diameter and turning 140 revolutions per minute, drives pulley B which is 10 inches in diameter. Keyed to the same shaft as B, pulley C, which is 6 inches in diameter, drives the 4-inch pulley D. Form proportions and solve for the speed of D.

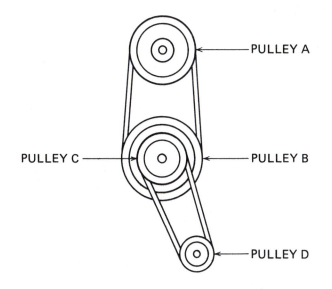

Unit 31 MISCELLANEOUS PROBLEMS

REVIEW OF BASIC PRINCIPLES

- Review units 51 to 53 in *Basic Mathematics Simplified* for the principles of ratio and proportion.

- Apply the principles of ratio and proportion to the work of the machinist by solving the Review Problems which follow.

REVIEW PROBLEMS

1. A joint 16 feet long requires 80 rivets, spaced as illustrated. How many rivets are required for a joint 11 feet long using the same spacing? _____

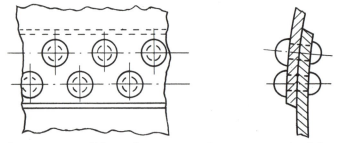

2. Under the same conditions, how many rivets are required for a joint 7 feet long? _____

3. If a joint 7 1/2 feet long requires 60 rivets and the same spacing is used in a joint 16 feet long, how many are required? _____

4. A shop employing 15 men is able to build 12 machines in one month. If the production schedule calls for 20 machines, how many men are required? _____

5. If 12 men build 8 machines in two weeks, how many men are required to build 12 machines in the same period? _____

6. A crew of 48 men assemble 105 machines in a year. How many men would be required to assemble 120 machines in the same period of time? _____

7. Fifty men are required to assemble 24 machines in six weeks. How large a working force would be required to assemble 30 machines in three weeks? _____

8. The output of a shop employing 240 men for a single year is 100 machines. At the same rate, how large a working force would be required to build 10 machines in a month? _____

9. Twelve men can do a job in 21 days working 8 hours a day. If the job must be completed in 14 days without increasing the number of hours per day, how many men must the contractor put on the job? _____

10. If 14 men, working 8 hours a day, can do a job in 15 days, how many days will be needed for 10 men working 7 hours a day to do the same job? _____

Note: The area of a circle varies directly with the square of the diameter.

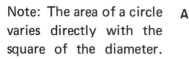
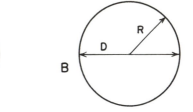

11. The area of a circle 3 inches in diameter is 7.0686 square inches. What is the area of a circle 7 inches in diameter?   _____

12. If the diameter of a circle is 6 2/3 inches, find its area.   _____

13. Find the area of a 15 3/4-inch diameter circle by comparing it to the area of a circle whose diameter is 1 inch.   _____

14. A circle has an area of 33.18315 square inches. Find the diameter of this circle by the method used in the preceding problems.   _____

Note: The tensile strength of a wire is in direct proportion to the area of its cross section, or to the square of its diameter.

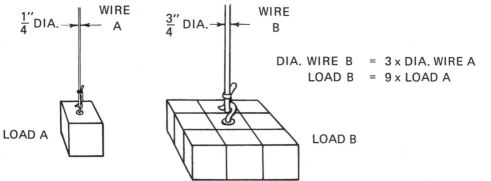

DIA. WIRE B   = 3 x DIA. WIRE A
LOAD B   = 9 x LOAD A

15. If a 3/8-inch wire supports a load of 2000 pounds, how much will a 9/16-inch wire support?   _____

16. A load of 49,000 pounds is carried by a 7/8-inch bar. If the load is increased to 125,000 pounds, what size bar will be required to carry it? Find the answer to the nearest 1/16 inch.   _____

17. How many times greater a load will a 1 1/2-inch bar carry than a 1/2-inch bar?   _____

18. The weight of a bar is in direct proportion to its length and the area of its cross section. A hexagonal bar 6 1/2 feet long with cross-sectional area of 2.34 square inches weighs 82 pounds. Find the weight of a hexagonal bar 9 1/4 feet long, if it has a cross section of 1.18 square inches.   _____

19. Which will carry the greater total load, three rods each 1 inch in diameter, or one rod 2 inches in diameter?   _____

20. A pump which discharges 4 gallons of water per minute can fill a tank in 20 hours. How long will it take a pump discharging 12 gallons per minute to fill it?   _____

Unit 32 BELT WIDTHS

REVIEW OF BASIC PRINCIPLES

- Review units 51 to 53 in *Basic Mathematics Simplified* for the principles of ratio and proportion as applied to belt widths.

- Apply the principles of ratio and proportion to the work of the machinist by solving the Review Problems which follow.

REVIEW PROBLEMS

Note: The width of belt required in power transmission varies directly with the horsepower and inversely with the speed of belt.

Form the proportion and solve the following:

1. If a 1-inch double belt traveling 600 feet per minute will transmit 1 horsepower, what width of belt is required to transmit 6 horsepower at 600 feet per minute?   _____

2. Find the width of belt required to transmit 1 horsepower at 200 feet per minute.   _____

3. At a speed of 450 feet per minute, how wide a belt is needed to transmit 1 horsepower?   _____

4. A belt which transmits 1 horsepower has a speed of 360 feet per minute.   Find the width of the belt.   _____

5. How wide a belt is needed to transmit 1 horsepower at 125 feet per minute?   _____

6. If a double belt traveling 600 feet per minute will transmit 1 horsepower for each inch of width, find the width of belt necessary to transmit 2 horsepower with belt speed of 1200 feet per minute.   _____

PRACTICAL MEASUREMENTS

Unit 33 AREAS OF RECTANGLES

BASIC PRINCIPLES OF AREAS OF RECTANGLES

- Study units 21 and 64 in *Basic Mathematics Simplified* for the principles applied for solving areas of rectangles.

- Apply the principles of area calculations to the work of the machinist by solving the Review Problems which follow.

REVIEW PROBLEMS

1. The tool crib in a machine shop is 14 feet long and 9 1/2 feet wide. How many square feet of floor space does it occupy?   _____

2. How many square inches are there in the piece of sheet metal as illustrated?   _____

3. If the sheet metal illustrated weighs 1 1/4 pounds per square foot, how much does the sheet weigh?   _____

21"

53"

4. A machine shop, as shown in the diagram, is 68 feet long by 41 1/2 feet wide. The rental is calculated at the rate of $1.60 per month per square foot of floor space. Deductions are made from the floor space for a stairwell 13 feet by 10 1/2 feet, and an elevator shaft which is 11 feet by 11 1/2 feet. What is the rent per month?   _____

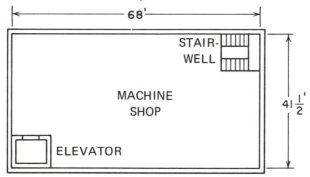

5. A man working on a surface grinder is paid at the rate of 3 cents per square inch of finished surface. The pieces he is grinding are rectangular in shape, 4 1/4 inches long by 2 3/4 inches wide. How much does he earn in an 8-hour day, if he finishes an average of 8 1/2 pieces per hour?   _____

6. Number 00 United States Standard Gage steel plate weighs 14.02 pounds per square foot. Find the weight of a number 00 plate that is 2 feet 7 inches by 3 feet 11 inches.   _____

Unit 34 AREAS OF PARALLELOGRAMS

BASIC PRINCIPLES OF PARALLELOGRAMS

- Review unit 21 in *Basic Mathematics Simplified* for the principles applied for solving of areas of parallelograms.

- Apply the principles of area calculation of parallelograms to the work of the machinist by solving the Review Problems which follow.

REVIEW PROBLEMS

1. The dovetail illustrated also shows the end of a gib. Find the area of the end of this gib.

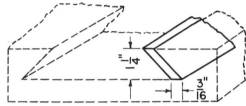

_____

2. A piece of sheet metal in the shape of a parallelogram is 3 feet 4 inches long and its altitude is 2 feet 7 inches. Find the area.

_____

3. The figure shows a piece of sheet metal, rectangular in shape, that had a parallelogram punched out of its center. From the dimensions given on the sketch, find the area of the piece that was punched out and the area of the part that is left.

_____

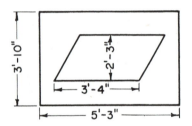

4. Four sections of wire grill were set up to enclose an area for a tool crib as shown in the figure A. Later they were moved and set up as shown in the figure B. How many more square feet of floor space did the tool crib occupy when it was square than when it was in the shape shown in figure B? What, if any, will be the change in area of grill required?

_____

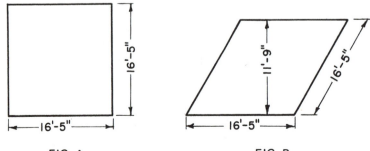

FIG. A   FIG. B

Unit 35 ANGLES

BASIC PRINCIPLES OF ANGLES

- Study unit 20 in *Basic Mathematics Simplified* for the principles applied for solving angles.

- Apply the principles for calculating angles to the work of the machinist by solving the Review Problems which follow.

REVIEW PROBLEMS

1. If the two straight lines AB and CD, as illustrated, cross at O and angle DOB is 37 degrees, what is angle AOC? What is angle AOD?

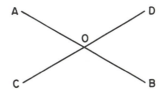

————————

————————

2. The piece of work shown in the following sketch is to be turned on a lathe. At what angle to the centerline of the work must the compound rest be set to turn an included angle of 120 degrees?

————————

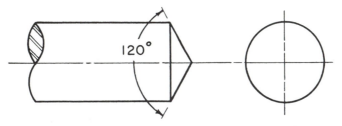

3. What is the angle that a plumb line will make with the top of a horizontal surface plate? Why?

————————

4. When turning a lathe center point as per sketch, at what angle to the centerline of lathe bed should the compound rest be set?

————————

5. In order to shape a piece of hexagonal stock as shown, at what angle from the vertical should the head be set?

————————

6. If the stock in the previous problem were planed in a vise, as illustrated, what angle from vertical would the head be set?

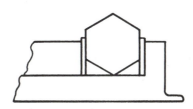

————————

7. When the cast iron piece B, is placed on an angle plate to be drilled, what should angle A be, to properly drill the hole?

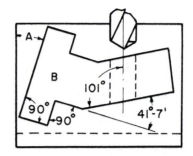

_____

8. The accompanying diagram shows a layout of five holes equally spaced on a 10-inch circle. What angle is formed by connecting the centers of holes B and C with the center?

_____

9. What angle does side A of a hexagonal bar make with the surface plate as illustrated?

_____

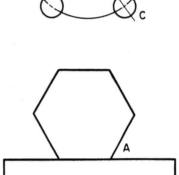

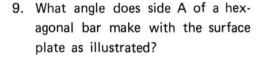

Note: Lines ad and bk are drawn parallel.

10. How many degrees in the sum of angles B, E, and F?   _____

11. Is angle F the same as angle A? Why?   _____

12. Is angle E the same as angle D? Why?   _____

13. Is angle E the same as angle C? Why?   _____

14. What is the sum of the degrees in the angles A, B, and C?   _____

15. If a pulley has twelve spokes, what is the angle between the centerlines of any two adjacent spokes? _____

16. How long should the sides of a 50-degree angle be drawn? _____

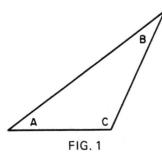

FIG. 1

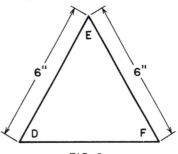

FIG. 2

17. angle A = 20 degrees angle B = 40 degrees Find angle C. _____

18. Angle B = 47 degrees 20 minutes Angle C = 110 degrees 14 minutes Find angle A. _____

19. Angle A = 17 degrees 21 minutes 43 seconds angle B = 27 degrees 52 minutes 51 seconds Find angle C. _____

20. Angle E = 70 degrees Find angle D and angle F. _____

21. Angle D = 35 degrees Find angle F and angle E. _____

22. Angle F = 19 degrees 41 minutes Find angle D and angle E. _____

Unit 36 AREAS OF TRIANGLES

BASIC PRINCIPLES OF SURFACE MEASURE

- Review unit 21 in *Basic Mathematics Simplified* for the principles of area measurement as applied to triangles.

- Apply the principles of area calculation to the work of the machinist by solving the Review Problems which follow.

REVIEW PROBLEMS

1. Find the area of a triangular piece of steel having a base of 23 inches and an altitude of 12 1/2 inches. _____

2. A triangle, with a base of 27 inches and an altitude of 17 inches, is cut from a piece of sheet metal four feet square. Find the area of the sheet metal left in the piece. _____

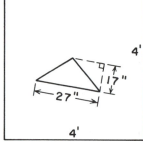

3. Two triangles are cut from a 4-foot square piece of sheet metal. One has a base of 2 1/4 feet and an altitude of 14 1/2 inches, and the other has a base of 19 1/2 inches and an altitude of 7 1/4 inches. Find the area of sheet metal left in the piece. _____

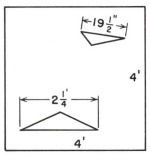

4. A triangular piece of sheet metal weighs 24 pounds. If the base of the triangle is 4 feet and its altitude is 6 feet, how much does the metal weigh per square foot? _____

5. What must be the height of a triangular piece of sheet metal to contain 100 square inches, if the base is 1 foot long? _____

6. Sheet metal weighing 2 1/2 pounds per square foot, is cut into a triangle with a base of 2 1/3 feet and an altitude of 2 feet 10 inches. Find the weight of the piece. _____

7. The base of a triangular steel plate is 26 1/2 inches long and its altitude is 15 3/4 inches. Find the area. _____

8. A triangular steel plate of the size and shape shown is to be carburized on one side. Find the area to be carburized. _____

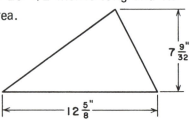

9. Sheet plate 3/16 inch thick weighs .053 pounds per square inch. What is the weight of a triangular plate with a base of 5 9/16 inches and an altitude of 4 5/8 inches?

10. The illustrated triangular steel plate has a square hole in it.   The hole measures 4 inches on each side. Find the number of square inches of metal in the piece.

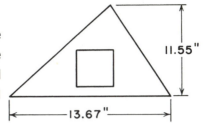

11. Triangular shaped pieces with a base of 6 1/6 inches and altitude 8 3/8 inches are blanked out of a strip 8 1/2 inches wide. If 8 pieces are blanked out of a strip 50 inches long, find the area of the pieces, and the area of the scrap metal.

The dimensions of five triangular steel plates are given in inches, in the following table. Find their weights.

	Base	Altitude	Thickness	Weight per square inch
12.	14.27	8.6	5/8	.175 pound
13.	11 3/32	19 1/16	3/4	.210 pound
14.	8.29	4.15	5/16	.087 pound
15.	125	47 5/16	7/16	.123 pound

Formula for area of an oblique triangle when the sides are known.

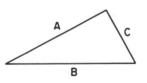

$$\text{Area} = \sqrt{S\,(S\text{-}A)\,(S\text{-}B)\,(S\text{-}C)}, \text{ when}$$
$$S = \frac{A + B + C}{2}$$

16. The sides of a triangular hole in a die measure 3.250 inches, 2.350 inches, and 1.750 inches. Find the area of a piece punched through this die.

17. Find the area of a triangular piece of sheet steel with sides 3 feet 2 inches, 2 feet 4 1/2 inches, and 4 feet 7 inches.

18. Find the cross section area of a bar of steel rolled in the triangular shape shown.

19. Sheet metal weighing 2 1/2 pounds per square foot is cut into a triangle with sides of 2 feet 4 inches, 1 foot 2 inches, and 2 feet 10 inches. Find the weight of the piece.

20. Find the area of the piece shown.

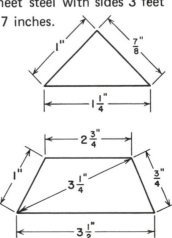

Unit 37 RIGHT TRIANGLES — HEXAGONS

BASIC PRINCIPLES OF RIGHT TRIANGLES

- Review units 21 and 59 in *Basic Mathematics Simplified* for the principles of surface measurement as applied to right triangles and hexagons.

- Apply the principles in dimensions for right triangles and hexagons to the work of the machinist by solving the Review Problems which follow.

REVIEW PROBLEMS

1. What is the distance between diagonally opposite corners of a machine base 6 1/2 feet by 4 1/2 feet?   _____

Find the diagonal distance between corners of the following rectangular pieces:

2. Length 6 feet 3 inches   Width 2 feet 3 inches   _____

3. Length 7 1/2 inches   Width 3 3/8 inches   _____

4. Length 13 1/8 inches   Width 4 3/4 inches   _____

5. Find the length of the brace needed in the sketch, if a is 14 inches and b is 17 inches. (Make no allowance for bends.)   _____

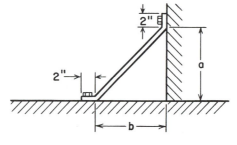

Find the length of the brace under the following conditions.   _____

6. a = 3 1/2 inches   b = 30 inches   _____

7. a = 2 feet 7 inches   b = 2 feet 3 inches   _____

8. On the illustrated template, find the distance between the centers of holes A and B.   _____

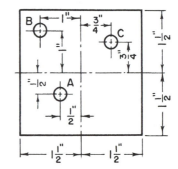

9. Find the distance center-to-center between holes A and C.   _____

10. Find the distance center-to-center between holes B and C.   _____

11. Find the distance from the center of hole A to the nearest corner. _____

12. Find the distance from the center of hole B to the nearest corner. _____

13. Find the distance from the center of hole C to the nearest corner. _____

14. How long is the diagonal of a square bar 2 inches on a side?   _____

15. Find the length of a side of the largest square section that can be milled from a round bar 2 inches in diameter. (See diagram.)

16. A piece of flat stock 3 inches wide has a diagonal of 3.354 inches. What is the thickness of the flat stock?

17. A block of steel, rectangular in section, and 1 inch thick, is milled from a piece of round stock. What is the greatest width obtainable, if the stock is 2 inches in diameter.

18. How many degrees in angle C of the triangle shown here?

19. What is the length of the side AC; of the side BC?

20. Find the length of the perpendicular CD.

21. Find the area of the triangle using

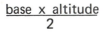

22. In any hexagon, as shown in the sketch, what is the value of angle AOB? Angle OAB? Angle OBA?

23. What is the distance across flats (CD) in the hexagon shown?

24. What is the area of the hexagon shown?

25. Find the sectional area of a hexagonal bar that measures 2 1/2 inches on a side.

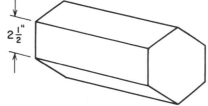

26. What is the length of side of the largest hexagon that can be milled from 3-inch round stock?

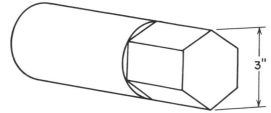

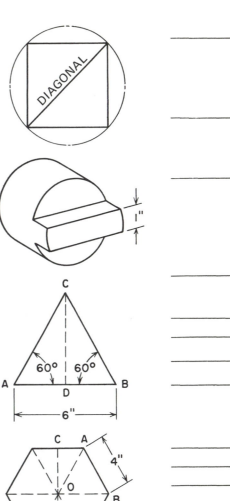

Unit 38 TRIANGLES – THREADS

BASIC PRINCIPLES OF THREADS

- Review units 63 and 66 in *Basic Mathematics Simplified* for the principles of formula calculation as applied to threads.

- Apply the principles of calculating by formulas to the work of the machinist by solving the Review Problems which follow.

REVIEW PROBLEMS

1. In the thread, as illustrated, if the pitch AC is 1 inch, what is the length AB and BC? _____ _____

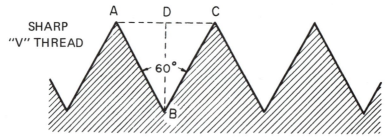

SHARP "V" THREAD

60°

2. What are the distances AD and DC? _____ _____

3. Determine the depth of DB. _____

SINGLE DEPTH

4. The "single depth" DB is the depth of thread on one side of the screw. To find the minor diameter, you must subtract from the outside diameter the "double depth," that is, the depth of thread on both sides of the screw. What is the "double depth" of a 1-inch pitch screw? _____

OUTSIDE DIAMETER

5. Find the single depth DB of a 1/8-inch pitch screw. _____

6. What is the double depth of a screw that has 8 threads to the inch? _____

1″ - 8 NC

7. Find the double depth of a screw with 5 threads per inch. _____

8. Find the minor diameter of a 3/8-inch screw having 16 threads per inch. _____

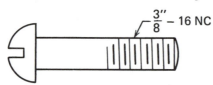

$\frac{3''}{8}$ – 16 NC

9. Find the minor diameter of a 3/4-inch – 8 National Coarse thread screw. _____

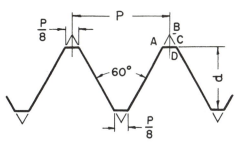

Note: On the American Standard Thread the crest and root of the thread are equal to 1/8 pitch.

10. Find the length of the flat AC for a standard 1-inch National Coarse thread (see diagram).   _____

11. By proportion in similar triangles, find BD for a 1-inch thread.   _____

12. How many times must BD be subtracted from the depth of a V thread to give the depth of an American Standard Thread?   _____

13. Find the double depth of a 1-inch pitch American National thread.   _____

    Note: To find the double depth of American National threads, divide the double depth of a 1-inch pitch thread by the number of threads per inch. This statement written as a formula is

    $$\text{Double Depth} = \frac{1.299}{\text{Numbers of threads per inch}}$$

    (This formula is for American National threads only.)

14. If the double depth of a 1-inch pitch National Coarse thread is 1.299, what is the double depth of a 1/9-inch pitch National Coarse thread?   _____

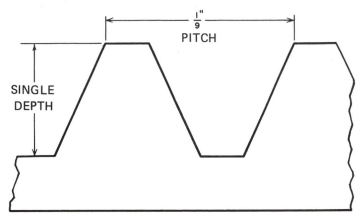

15. What is the double depth of a 1/16-inch pitch American National thread?   _____

16. What is the double depth of a 1/11-inch pitch American National thread?   _____

17. What is the double depth of a 1/18-inch pitch American National thread?   _____

18. What is the double depth of a 1/13-inch pitch American National thread?   _____

Unit 39 REVIEW PROBLEMS

REVIEW OF BASIC PRINCIPLES ON PRACTICAL MEASUREMENTS

- Review units 20, 21, and 59 in *Basic Mathematics Simplified* for the principles of angular and circular measurement, surface measurement, and square root.

- Apply the principles of measurement to the work of the machinist by solving the Review Problems which follow.

REVIEW PROBLEMS

1. The accompanying drawing shows a steel plate 1/4 inch thick. What is the shape of the plate? What is its area?

2. Find the height of an equilateral triangle that measures one foot on a side.

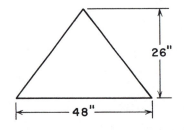

3. Find the distance between the centers of the two pulleys as illustrated.

4. A sharp "V" thread has the cross section of an equilateral triangle. If the pitch is 1/12 inch, find the single depth.

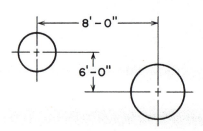

5. A piece of square stock measures 1 3/8 inches on a side. What is the distance across the corners?

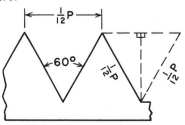

VEE THREAD SECTION

6. Find the center-to-center distance A between the bolt holes of the plate, as illustrated.

7. The area of a triangle is 863 square inches and the altitude is 54 inches. What is the length of the base?

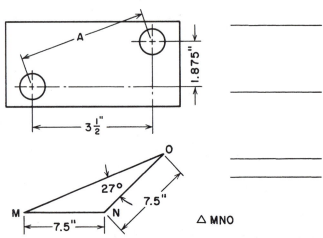

8. Find the number of degrees in each of the angles N and M, in the triangle MNO.

9. Find the number of degrees in each of the angles TOZ and FOM shown in the figure.

_____

10. Find the area of an isoceles right triangle when its hypotenuse is 3.5 inches.

_____

11. How far is it from a corner to the center of the opposite side of a triangular steel bar 2 1/2 inches on a side?

_____

12. How deep are the threads on a 5/8-inch − 11 "V" thread screw?

_____

13. How many degrees are there in angle DEF of the octagon shown in the figure?

_____

14. How many degrees are there in an angle between any two adjacent sides of a hexagon?

_____

15. A steel plate, triangular in shape, is laid out, with base 17.546 inches, altitude 8.66 inches, and angle B 30 degrees. (See figure.) Find the length of sides M and N for checking the layout.

_____

16. Find the cross-sectional area of the metal in this square tube.

_____

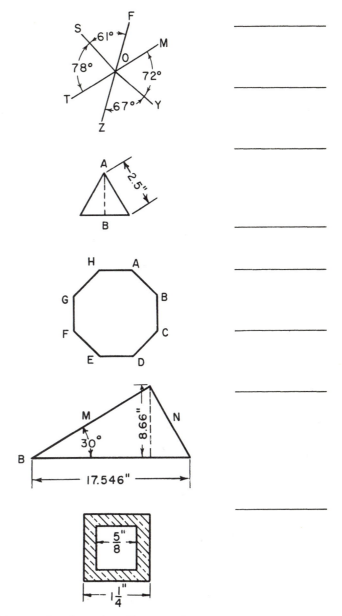

17. Calculate the area of the hole punched in a strip of steel as illustrated.

_____

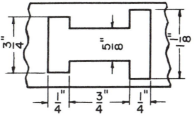

18. What is the area of the "T" slot as illustrated?

_____

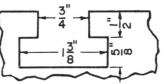

19. Find the area of the punching as shown in the accompanying sketch.

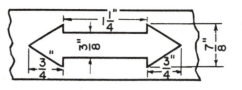

_____

20. Find the cross-sectional area of the steel I-beam.

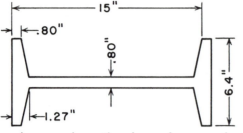

_____

21. Six holes are drilled, evenly spaced, on the circumference of a 14-inch circle.

   a.   What is the distance between each hole, center to center?

   _____

   b.   What angle is made between a radius line and a line joining two adjacent holes?

   _____

22. Find the area of a hexagon 1 inch on a side, by dividing it into 6 equilateral triangles.

   _____

23. What is the distance across the corners of a hexagonal nut 1 inch on a side?

   _____

24. What size blank is needed to mill a hexagon 2 1/2 inches across the flats?

   _____

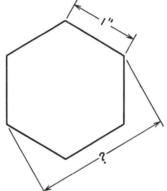

25. A job requires four holes to be spaced equidistant around a 3-inch diameter circle. What is the chordal distance between hole centers?

   _____

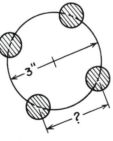

26. In order to make a hexagonal piece 1 1/2 inches across the sides, what size must the blank be turned before cutting the sides?

   _____

Unit 40 CIRCLES

BASIC PRINCIPLES OF CIRCLES

- Review unit 20 in *Basic Mathematics Simplified* for principles applied to circular measure, and unit 21 for principles applied to surface measure.

- Apply the principles of circular measure to the work of the machinist by solving the Review Problems which follow.

REVIEW PROBLEMS

1. If angle ACE in figure 1 is 20 degrees, find the following angles: ABE, ADE, OAG, BAF, BDA, AOE.

FIG. 1

2. How many degrees in angle ABP in figure 2?

3. If AB is 1 1/2 inches and the radius of the larger circle is 3 inches, find distance PB.

4. If angle ROB is 60 degrees, what is the value of angle AOR in figure 3?

FIG. 2

5. What is the value of angle ABO?

6. If AC is 2 inches, what length is CB?

7. If AC is 4 inches and radius OB is 5 inches, what is the length of OC?

FIG. 3

8. What is the length of RC?

9. In figure 4, angle BEA is 37 degrees 42 minutes. Find angle CED.

10. Find angle BEC.

11. AE = 6 inches   EC = 2 inches
    BE = 3 inches   Find ED.

FIG. 4

12. Find the circumference of the pulley as illustrated.

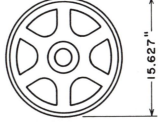

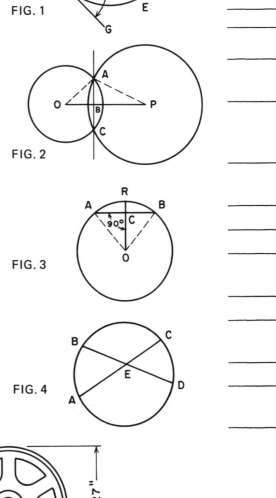

13. A piece of 3 5/16-inch round stock is turned on a lathe. How long an unbroken chip does the tool take off for each revolution of the workpiece?
_____

14. The diameter of the pitch circle of a gear is 5 1/8 inches. Find the circumference of the pitch circle.
_____

15. The outside diameter of the gear in the preceding problem is 5 1/4 inches. What is the circumference of the outside diameter?
_____

16. The circumference of a grinding wheel is 2 feet 2 1/2 inches. Find its diameter.
_____

17. A steel spring has 9 complete coils. If the spring is 1.328 inches in diameter, how long a piece of wire is required to make it? The diameter given is the average of the inside and outside diameters of the spring.
_____

18. A piece of steel spring wire 17 3/4 inches long is wound into a coil spring having a pitch diameter (average diameter) of .927 inch. How many coils does the spring have?
_____

19. The flat cast iron plate shown has a 3 3/4-inch round hole in it. Find the area of the cast iron.
_____

20. A steel disk 7 1/2 inches in diameter by 3/8 inch thick is to be carbonized on its flat surfaces only. Find the area that is to be carbonized.
_____

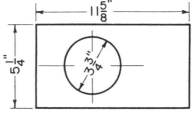

21. Twenty-seven circular blanks 3 5/16 inches in diameter are punched out of a strip of sheet metal 3 1/2 inches wide by 7 feet long. Find the area of one of the blanks and the area of material that is wasted. Allow 1/16 inch on each side of blanks to insure against defective stamping.
_____
_____

22. A circular blower opening is covered by a heavy wire screen. The diameter of the opening is 3 feet 7 inches. If the screen is cut from a piece four feet square, find the area that is wasted, and the area of the piece that is used to cover the opening.
_____

23. The circular steel plate, as illustrated, is 3/8 inch thick, with a radius of 9 1/2 inches. Each of the four holes is 5 3/8 inches in diameter. Find the weight of the plate. (Refer to the table of weights for steel plate given in a trade handbook.)
_____

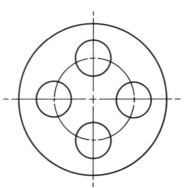

24. A round steel bar will support a load of 40,000 pounds per square inch of its cross section. If the bar is 7/8 inch in diameter, how much will it support?
_____

Unit 41 CIRCLES, SEGMENTS, SECTORS, ELLIPSES

REVIEW OF BASIC PRINCIPLES OF CIRCLES, SEGMENTS, SECTORS, ELLIPSES

- Review units 21 and 65 in *Basic Mathematics Simplified* for the principles of circles, segments, sectors, and ellipses.
- Apply the principles of circular calculation to the work of the machinist by solving the Review Problems which follow.

REVIEW PROBLEMS

1. Find the area of a ring with an outside diameter of 3 1/2 inches and an inside diameter of 1 3/4 inches.

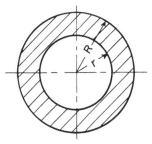

_____

2. The outside diameter of a flywheel rim is 3 1/2 feet, the inside diameter of the rim is 2 feet 10 inches. Find the cross-sectional area of the rim.

Area (A) of Ring
$$A = \pi (R^2 - r^2)$$

_____

3. A 14-inch diameter grinding wheel has a center hole 2 inches in diameter. Find the area of a side of the wheel.

_____

4. Find the area of a sector of 40 degrees with a radius of 8 inches.

_____

5. A 6-foot template is shown. Find its area.

_____

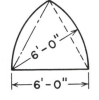

TEMPLATE FORM

6. The diagram shows a 70-foot water hose mounted on the outside of a machine shop wall, in the center of the wall which is 80 feet long. Find the maximum area in square yards in which the water hose may be used outside the building.

_____

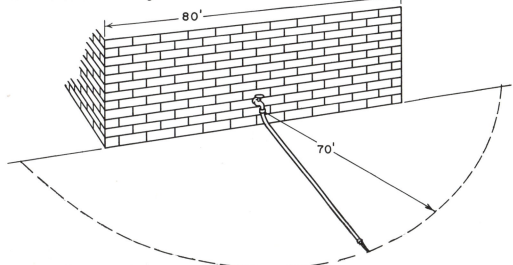

In the figure shown, chord AB is 6 inches and rise is 2 inches.

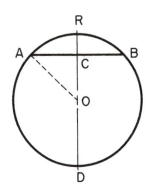

7. What is the length of AC, CB? _____

8. Knowing AC, CB, and RC, find CD. (Properties of circles.) _____

9. What is the length of diameter RD? _____

10. What is the length of radius AO? _____

11. With chord AB of 2 inches and RC 6 inches, find radius. _____

Note: To machine the workpiece shown in the drawing, it is fastened to the face plate of a lathe. Its arc AB is finished by boring.

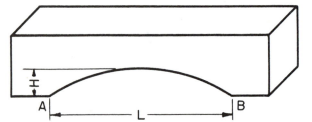

12. If L is 5 inches and H is 2 inches, find the distance that points A and B must be located from the center of the face plate. _____

13. L is 2 1/8 inches; H is 15/16 inch. Find the location of A and B from center. _____

14. L is 3.375 inches; H is .742 inch. Find the location of A and B from center. _____

15. L is 6.40 inches; H is 1.687 inches. Find the location of A and B from center. _____

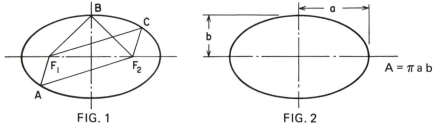

FIG. 1   FIG. 2

An ellipse is a figure bounded by a curved line such that the distance from any point on the line to two fixed points within the line is constant.

In figure 1: F_1 B plus BF_2 = F_1 C plus CF_2 = F_1 A plus AF_2

Area A (figure 2) = π × 1/2 long axis (a) × 1/2 short axis (b).

16. If A equals 2 inches and B equals 1 inch, find the area of an ellipse. _____

17. An elliptical pulley arm measures 3 inches wide and 1 3/4 inches thick. Find area of cross section. _____

18. Find the area of an ellipse with long axis 6 feet 4 inches, short axis 4 feet 3 1/2 inches. _____

19. Find the area of an ellipse with long diameter 1.325 inches, short diameter .750 inch.   _____

20. Find the area of an ellipse with major (long) axis 14 7/8 inches, and short (minor) axis 10 1/2 inches.   _____

21. Find the area of an ellipse with major axis 25 1/2 feet, minor axis 15 feet 8 inches.   _____

22. In figure 3, what is the area of the square?   _____

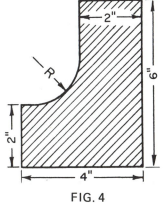
FIG. 3

23. What is the area of the sector?   _____

24. What is the area of the cross hatched part?   _____

25. In figure 4, with R equal to 1 inch, find area of piece to three decimal places.   _____

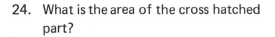
FIG. 4

26. Find area of piece, with R equal to 1 1/2 inches.   _____

27. Find area of piece, with R equal to 7/8 inch.   _____

Unit 42 CIRCLES — PRACTICAL PROBLEMS

REVIEW OF BASIC PRINCIPLES OF CIRCLES

- Review units 21, 59, and 65 in *Basic Mathematics Simplified* for the principles of circular measurement.

- Apply the principles of circles to the work of the machinist by solving the Review Problems which follow.

REVIEW PROBLEMS

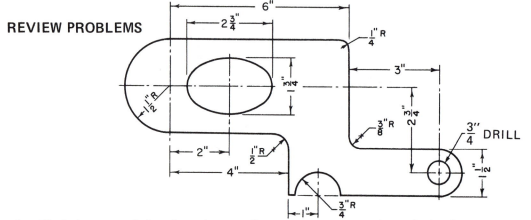

1. Find the area of the piece shown. Carry answer out to three decimal places. _____

2. A duct, 14 inches square inside, encloses four round pipes of equal size which fit closely into the duct. What percent of the space is occupied by the pipes? _____

3. If one mile per minute is the safe surface speed of an abrasive wheel, what are the maximum revolutions per minute that a 9-inch wheel should be turned? _____

4. Determine the maximum revolutions per minute for a 24-inch abrasive wheel. _____

5. Three circles are enclosed in an equilateral triangle. If the circles have a 10-inch radius, find the sides of the triangle. _____

6. Find the area of the part of the triangle which is not occupied by the circles. _____

7. Compare the area of a circle 1 inch in diameter with the area of a circle 2 inches in diameter. _____

8. If holes are cut in the 14-inch diameter cast iron disk, shown in the sketch, what is the total area reduction? What percent reduction? _____ _____

4 HOLES 2" DIA.

4" DIA.

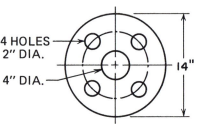

9. Calculate the area of a brass punching shaped as shown in the sketch.

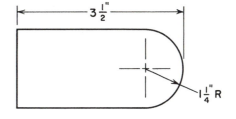

_____

10. What is the area of metal in the key section as illustrated?

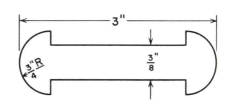

_____

11. Four steel plates 22 inches in diameter are cut from a piece of boiler plate four feet square. How much stock is wasted?

_____

12. The sectional area of a piston is 63.6 square inches. What is its diameter?

_____

13. The steam gage on an engine indicates that the cylinder pressure is 112 pounds to the square inch. If the diameter of the piston is 10 1/2 inches, what is the total pressure of steam against the piston?

_____

14. Which has the greater area, a square iron plate measuring 8 inches on a side or a circular brass disk 9 inches in diameter?

_____

15. What is the largest square that can be cut on a shaft 2.25 inches in diameter?

_____

16. What size round stock must be selected so that a square nut 4 1/2 inches on a side may be cut from it?

_____

17. What diameter round stock is needed to mill a hexagon which measures .500 inch across the flats?

_____

18. In milling a hexagon nut on a 1 15/16-inch diameter bar, how deep should the cut be made from the outside surface of the bar?

_____

19. What is the distance around the edge of a lathe face plate which is 46 inches in diameter?

_____

20. An abrasive wheel is 8 inches in diameter. How many feet will a point on the circumference travel while the wheel is making one revolution?

_____

21. A resinoid bonded cut off wheel should have a surface velocity of 5500 feet per minute. Find the number of revolutions per minute of a cut off wheel 9 inches in diameter.

_____

Unit 43 RECTANGULAR SOLIDS

BASIC PRINCIPLES OF RECTANGULAR SOLIDS

- Study unit 22 and review unit 64 in *Basic Mathematics Simplified* for the principles of rectangular solids.

- Apply the principles of volume measure of rectangular solids to the work of the machinist by solving the Review Problems which follow.

REVIEW PROBLEMS

Unless otherwise specified, the listed weights in pounds or fractions of a pound are to be used for metals called for in the following problems.

	Weight Per Cubic Inch	Weight Per Cubic Foot
Steel	0.283	489.0
Cast Iron	0.2600	449.2
Bronze	0.3195	552.2
Brass	0.3018	521.7
Wrought Iron	0.2834	489.8

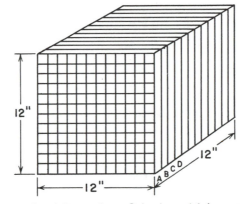

1. What is the area of the front of the prism shown? _____

2. If slice A, 1 inch thick, is cut from the prism shown, how many 1-inch cube blocks are in this slice? _____

3. If two slices A and B are cut from the prism, find the number of cubic inches in the two pieces. _____

4. How many cubic inches are contained in a piece 3 inches thick cut from this prism? _____

5. How many cubic inches in the entire prism shown? _____

6. What is the volume, in cubic inches, of a 1-foot cube? _____

7. What is the area of the end of a piece of 3/4" x 1 1/2" steel bar? _____

8. Find the volume of a piece of 3/4" x 1 1/2" steel bar which is 6 inches long. _____

9. Find the difference in cubic inches between 3 cubic feet and a 3-foot cube. _____

10. Find the volume of a piece of flat stock 3/4 inch by 2 inches by 10 inches long. _____

11. If steel weighs .283 pounds per cubic inch, find the weight of the piece in the preceding problem. _____

12. Find the weight of a piece of steel 9/16 inch by 2 inches by 4 feet 2 inches. _____

13. What length must a piece of 2-inch square steel bar be cut to weigh exactly 5 pounds? _____

14. A piece 3 inches wide and 2 1/2 feet long weighs approximately 8 pounds. Find the thickness to the nearest 1/16 inch. _____

15. A piece of square steel 4 feet long weighs 6 1/2 pounds. Find its width to the nearest 1/16 inch. _____

16. A rectangular box, similar to the sketch, is made of 1/8-inch sheet metal. Find the weight of the box, if outside dimensions are 4 feet by 3.4 feet by 2.6 feet, and the steel used weighs .29 pound per cubic inch. The box has a bottom, but no top. _____

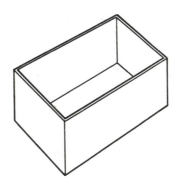

17. To line the bottom and sides of a cubical box, 180 square feet of zinc are required. How many cubic feet of water will it hold? _____

18. Find the cost at 40 cents per pound for sheet copper to line the bottom and sides of a cubical box 7 feet on an edge, if the copper sheets weigh 12 ounces per square foot. _____

19. Find the weight of a piece of steel 1/16 inch thick, 2 feet wide, and 4 feet long. _____

20. Find the weight of a piece of number 11 gage (United States Standard) steel 1 foot 1 inch wide and 3 feet 1/2 inch long. _____

21. A piece of 22 gage (United States Standard) steel 4 1/2 feet long weighs 20 pounds. Find its width. _____

22. A piece of sheet steel 2 feet by 6 feet weighs 9.14 pounds. Find the thickness to the nearest thousandth. What gage is this? _____
_____

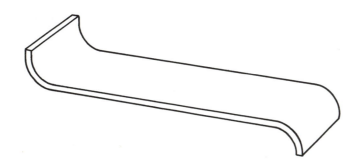

Unit 44 CYLINDERS

REVIEW OF BASIC PRINCIPLES OF VOLUME MEASURE

- Review units 22 and 65 in *Basic Mathematics Simplified.*

- Apply the principles of volume measure of cylinders to the work of the machinist by solving the Review Problems which follow.

REVIEW PROBLEMS

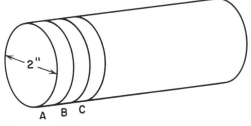

Volume of Cylinder = area of base x height

1. What is the area of the end of the 2-inch diameter cylinder shown? _____

2. If slice A, 1 inch long, is cut from the cylinder, how many cubic inches in the slice? _____

3. If three slices, A, B, and C each 1 inch long are cut from the cylinder, how many cubic inches do the three contain? _____

4. Find the volume of a piece of 2-inch diameter rod 14 inches long. _____

5. Using .283 pound per cubic inch, find the weight of a 3/4-inch round bar 20 feet long. _____

6. If the volume of a 3-inch diameter cylinder is 49.48 cubic inches, find the length in inches. _____

7. Find the length of a 1 1/8-inch diameter cylinder with a volume of 5.467 cubic inches. _____

8. Find the diameter of a piece of steel 14 inches long, having a volume of 8.418 cubic inches. _____

9. How many square feet of sheet metal are required for each end of the cylindrical tank illustrated? _____

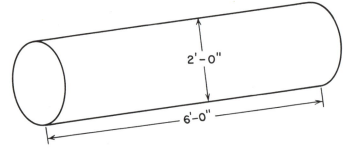

10. How many square feet of sheet metal are used in a piece 6 feet long forming the side of the tank, allowing nothing for lap? _____

11. How many square feet of sheet metal are used in making the complete tank in the preceding problem, allowing nothing for laps? _____

12. Find the number of cubic feet of coolant the tank in problem 10 will hold. _____

13. In drilling soft steel, a 1 9/16-inch drill makes 37 revolutions per minute with a feed of .012 inch per revolution. How far does the drill advance in 3 1/2 minutes? _____

14. A 3/16-inch drill makes 2037 revolutions per minute with a feed of .004 inch per revolution. How far does the drill advance in 1/2 minute? _____

15. A 1 1/2-inch drill turns 153 revolutions per minute with a feed of .012 inch while drilling a rectangular block of steel 2 inches by 3 inches by 3 inches. Find the weight of steel removed in 2 minutes. Use .283 pound as weight of steel per cubic inch. _____

16. How many revolutions will be necessary to take one cut 36 inches long on a shaft, with a feed of .015 inch per revolution? _____

17. A shaft 6 feet long is turned at the rate of 50 revolutions per minute, with a feed of .050 inch per revolution. How long will it take for a complete cut, allowing one minute for changing the lathe dog from one end to the other? _____

18. In turning a steel shaft 6 inches in diameter and 4 feet long, the cutting speed was 90 feet per minute and the feed .020 inch per revolution. Find the time required for a cut 3 feet long. _____

19. A piece of stock is turned on a lathe from 2 1/4 inches down to 1 3/4 inches in diameter. If the cut is 7 inches long, how many cubic inches of metal are removed? _____

20. The cylindrical piece of steel, as illustrated, is to be carbonized on its lateral surface as part of the heat treating process it is to go through. Find the area to be carbonized. _____

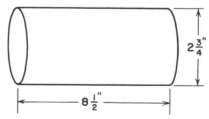

21. A 1 1/8-inch arbor, 10 inches long overall, is turned undersize for a distance of 1 1/4 inches on each end. The lateral surface between the two undersize ends is to be ground. Find the area of the surface to be ground. _____

22. A tank for a hardening bath is 2 feet 4 inches in diameter and 2 feet 8 inches deep. How many gallons of liquid will be required to fill the tank to within 5 inches of the top? A gallon contains 231 cubic inches. _____

Unit 45 REVIEW PROBLEMS – SOLIDS

REVIEW OF BASIC PRINCIPLES OF VOLUME MEASURE

- Review units 22, 64, and 65 in *Basic Mathematics Simplified* for the principles of volume measure applied to practical measurements.

- Apply the principles of volume measure to the work of the machinist by solving the Review Problems which follow.

REVIEW PROBLEMS

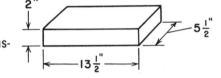

1. What is the volume of the illustrated casting?

_____

2. How many cubic inches of metal are removed in boring a 2-inch diameter hole through a flat piece of steel 1 1/2 inches thick, as illustrated.

_____

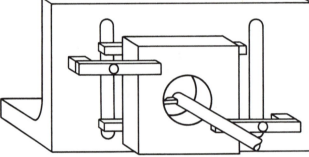

3. What is the volume of the cast iron sleeve, as illustrated?

_____

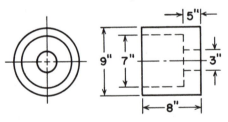

4. How many cubic inches in the brass bushing as shown in the accompanying drawing.

_____

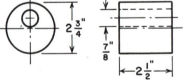

5. How many cubic inches of cast iron are there in the part illustrated?

_____

6. How many cubic inches are there in the brass blank for a hexagonal nut, as shown in the sketch?

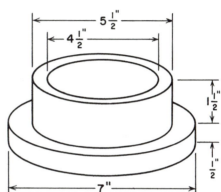

$\frac{29}{32}$"

$\frac{7}{16}$"

_____

7. Find the number of cubic inches of steel in the hexagonal bar shown.

$5\frac{1}{4}$"

$\frac{3}{4}$"

_____

8. What is the volume of metal in the bronze ring, as illustrated?

9. Determine the cubic inches of metal per foot of length in a copper tube with an outside diameter of 2 inches and an inside diameter of 1 1/2 inches.

10. What is the volume of a steel shaft 6 inches in diameter and 20 feet long?

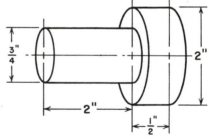

$5\frac{1}{2}$"

$4\frac{1}{2}$"

$1\frac{1}{2}$"

$\frac{1}{2}$"

7"

_____

_____

_____

11. The pin in the accompanying sketch is to be made of steel. Determine the number of cubic inches in 408 such pins.

$\frac{3}{4}$"

2"

2"

$\frac{1}{2}$"

_____

12. A cast iron sleeve, as shown in the diagram, has a cored hole 1 inch by 4 inches which extends through its entire length. How many cubic inches of iron are there in this sleeve?

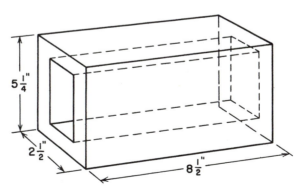

$5\frac{1}{4}$"

$2\frac{1}{2}$"

$8\frac{1}{2}$"

_____

Unit 46 CONES

BASIC PRINCIPLES OF CONES

- Review units 20, 21, 22, and 65 in *Basic Mathematics Simplified.*

- Apply the principles of angular, circular, and volume measure to the work of the machinist by solving the Review Problems which follow.

REVIEW PROBLEMS

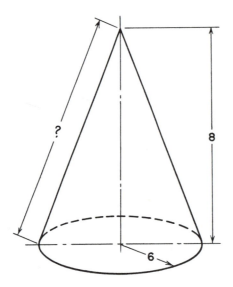

Note: Lateral area of a cone = perimeter of base x 1/2 the slant height.
Volume of a cone = the area of the base x 1/3 the altitude.

1. Determine the slant height of the illustrated cone. _____

2. Find the perimeter of the base. _____

3. What is the lateral area of the cone? _____

4. Find the area of the base. _____

5. What is the total area of the given cone? _____

6. What is the volume of the given cone? _____

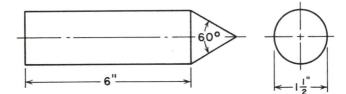

7. Find the overall length of the piece in the illustration. _____

8. Find the volume of the cylindrical part. _____

9. Find the volume of the cone. _____

10. Using steel at .283 pound per cubic inch, find the weight of the piece. _____

Unit 47 CIRCULAR RINGS

BASIC PRINCIPLES OF CIRCULAR RINGS

- Review unit 65 in *Basic Mathematics Simplified* for the principles of circular measure.
- Apply the principles of circular measure to the work of the machinist by solving the Review Problems which follow.

REVIEW PROBLEMS

Note: A solid ring is made with a piece of stock bent into circular form, the cross section of which may be either a circle, square, rectangle, or any other shape. The length of stock required equals the length of the centerline of the ring.

The area (A) of any solid ring equals the perimeter of cross section times the length of centerline.

$$A = \pi D \times (2B + 2C) \qquad\qquad A = \pi D \times \pi E$$

The volume (V) of any solid ring equals the area of cross section times length of centerline.

$$V = \pi D \times BC \qquad\qquad V = \pi D \times \pi R^2$$

1. Find length of 1/2-inch round stock needed to form a ring 3.500 inches inside diameter. _____

2. The cross section of a solid wrought iron ring is a circle of 4 inch radius. The inner radius of the ring is 3 feet. Find the area of the surface of the ring. _____

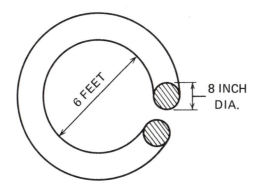

3. Find the volume of the ring in the preceding problem. _____

4. Find the surface area of a ring made of 1-inch round steel which has an outside diameter of 10 inches. _____

Unit 48 MEASURING IRREGULAR FORMS

BASIC PRINCIPLES OF IRREGULAR FORMS

- Review units 21 and 66 in *Basic Mathematics Simplified* for the principles of irregular forms.

- Apply the principles of surface measure and special formulas to the work of the machinist by solving the Review Problems which follow.

REVIEW PROBLEMS

Note: To find the approximate area of a surface between a curve and a straight line (figure 1) or a surface bounded by a curve (figure 2), divide the base line AY into any number of equal parts (AC, CE, EG). From these points erect perpendiculars (AB, CD, EF) intersecting the opposite boundary. At the center of each of these parts, draw ordinates (i j, k l, m n).

Take the average length of all ordinates and multiply by the length of the base line.

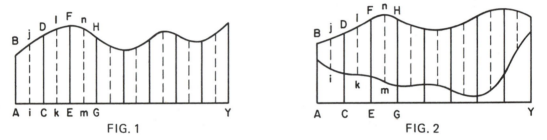

FIG. 1   FIG. 2

Note: Another way to find the approximate area between a curve and a straight line of a piece bounded by a curve is to use Simpson's Rule.

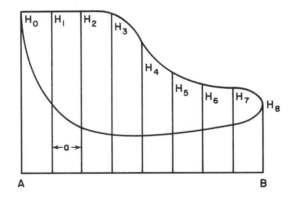

SIMPSON'S RULE

Divide the base AB into any *even* number of equal parts and measure the ordinates at each point. Add together the first and last ordinates, twice the sum of the other *even* ordinates and four times the sum of the *odd* ordinates. Multiply the sum by one-third the distance between consecutive ordinates. The result is the approximate area.

$$\text{Area} = 1/3\, a\, (H_0 + 4H_1 + 2H_2 + 4H_3 + 2H_4 + 4H_5 + 2H_6 + 4H_7 + H_8)$$

Note: The instructor should supply patterns which require the use of the formula to find the area of an irregular form.

Unit 49 HORSEPOWER

REVIEW OF BASIC PRINCIPLES

- Review units 63 and 66 in *Basic Mathematics Simplified.*
- Apply the use of formulas in the solution of problems to the work of the machinist by solving the Review Problems which follow.

REVIEW PROBLEMS

Note: The indicated horsepower developed in one end of the cylinder of a steam engine is found by the formula:

$$\text{Horsepower} = \frac{PLAN}{33000}$$

P = mean effective pressure in pounds per square inch.

L = length of stroke in feet.

A = area of end of piston in square inches.

N = number of strokes per minute.

1. Find the horsepower when P equals 65 pounds per square inch, L equals 2 feet, A equals 30 square inches, and N equals 55. _____

2. Find the horsepower when P equals 40 pounds per square inch, L equals 24 inches, A equals 29.5 square inches, and N equals 75. _____

3. Find the indicated horsepower in the head end of an engine having a stroke of 21 inches in a cylinder 6 inches in diameter with an effective mean pressure of 45 pounds per square inch and 85 strokes per minute. _____

4. If horsepower = 25, what is the value of (PLAN)? _____

5. If horsepower equals 10, L equals 2 feet, A equals 24 square inches, N equals 80, find value of P. _____

6. If horsepower equals 5, P equals 70 pounds per square inch, A equals 20 square inches, and N equals 100, find the length of the stroke. _____

7. Horsepower equals 15, L equals 1 1/2 feet, P equals 45 pounds per square inch, and N equals 125. Find the value of A. _____

8. What area of cylinder is necessary to develop 20 horsepower with a stroke of 18 inches, pressure of 45 pounds per square inch, and 100 strokes per minute? _____

Unit 50 HORSEPOWER AND TAP DRILL FORMULAS

REVIEW OF BASIC PRINCIPLES

- Review units 63 and 66 in *Basic Mathematics Simplified.*

- Apply the use of formulas to the work of the machinist by solving the Review Problems which follow.

REVIEW

Note: The Society of Automotive Engineers (S.A.E.) formula for approximate horsepower (h.p.) of a gas engine is based on piston speed of 1000 feet per minute is as follows:

$$\text{h.p.} = \frac{D^2 N}{2.5}$$

D = diameter of cylinder   N = number of cylinders

1. D = 4 inches   N = 4   Find horsepower.   _____

2. Horsepower = 30   D = 3 1/2 inches   Find N.   _____

3. Horsepower = 45   N = 6   Find D.   _____

4. What horsepower is developed by a six-cylinder engine with a 3 1/8 inch bore?   _____

5. How many 4 3/8 inch cylinders will produce 60 horsepower?   _____

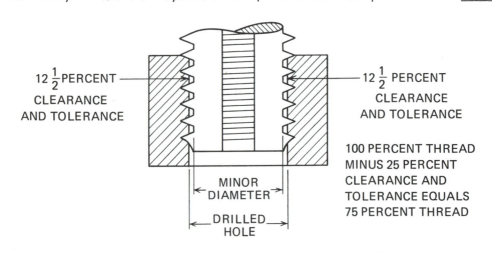

$12\frac{1}{2}$ PERCENT CLEARANCE AND TOLERANCE

$12\frac{1}{2}$ PERCENT CLEARANCE AND TOLERANCE

100 PERCENT THREAD MINUS 25 PERCENT CLEARANCE AND TOLERANCE EQUALS 75 PERCENT THREAD

MINOR DIAMETER

DRILLED HOLE

Note: One method of finding tap drill size for easy tapping of American National threads is to subtract the thread pitch from the outside diameter of the tap. This gives approximately 75 percent thread engagement.

$$d = D - \frac{1}{N} - ?$$

d = tap drill size   D = major diameter   N = number of threads per inch

6. Find tap drill size for a 5/8-inch National Coarse thread.   _____

7. Find tap drill size for a 1-inch National Coarse thread.   _____

Unit 51 TAPER PIN AND GEAR FORMULAS

REVIEW OF BASIC PRINCIPLES

- Review units 63 and 66 in *Basic Mathematics Simplified*.
- Apply the formulas for pins and gears to the work of the machinist by solving the Review Problems which follow.

REVIEW PROBLEMS

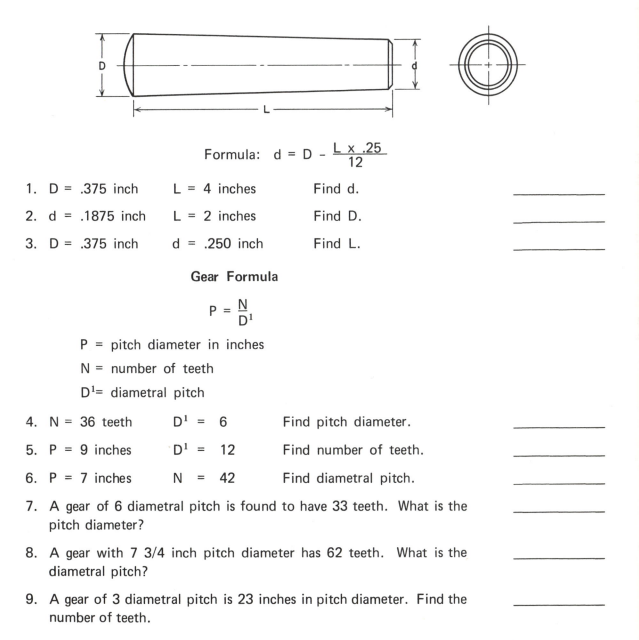

Formula: $d = D - \dfrac{L \times .25}{12}$

1. D = .375 inch   L = 4 inches   Find d.   _____

2. d = .1875 inch   L = 2 inches   Find D.   _____

3. D = .375 inch   d = .250 inch   Find L.   _____

Gear Formula

$$P = \frac{N}{D^1}$$

P = pitch diameter in inches

N = number of teeth

D^1= diametral pitch

4. N = 36 teeth D^1 = 6   Find pitch diameter.   _____

5. P = 9 inches D^1 = 12   Find number of teeth.   _____

6. P = 7 inches   N = 42   Find diametral pitch.   _____

7. A gear of 6 diametral pitch is found to have 33 teeth. What is the   _____
    pitch diameter?

8. A gear with 7 3/4 inch pitch diameter has 62 teeth. What is the   _____
    diametral pitch?

9. A gear of 3 diametral pitch is 23 inches in pitch diameter. Find the   _____
    number of teeth.

Unit 52 REVIEW PROBLEMS

REVIEW OF BASIC FORMULAS

- Review units 63-67 in *Basic Mathematics Simplified* for the formation and application of formulas.

- Apply the principle of formulas to the work of the machinist by solving the Review Problems which follow.

REVIEW PROBLEMS

Note: Use formulas to solve the following problems. First set down the formula, then substitute the given quantities, and show as many steps in the solution of the equation as is necessary to make it clear and understandable.

1. Find the horsepower of a single steam engine which has the following specifications: mean effective pressure, 140 pounds per square inch; length of stroke, 16 inches; piston diameter, 9 1/2 inches; revolutions per minute, 1100.   _____

2. A piece of work in a lathe is turning at the rate of 375 revolutions per minute. Find the cutting speed of the lathe tool, if the piece is 2 7/8 inches in diameter.   _____

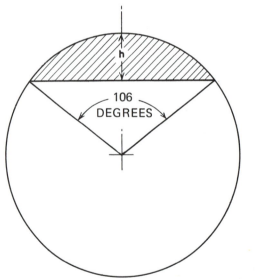

3. A chord 8 inches long is drawn in a circle, as illustrated. The distance h, from the center of the chord to the circumference, is 2 inches. Find the area of the sector, if the angle enclosing the sector is 106 degrees.   _____

4. The melting point of pure iron is 1505 degrees centigrade. What Fahrenheit temperature is this? (F = 9/5C + 32°)   _____

5. Steel which is heated to a cherry red is 1650 degrees Fahrenheit. What centigrade temperature is this?   _____

Unit 53 FUNDAMENTAL CONSTRUCTIONS

BASIC PRINCIPLES OF CONSTRUCTION

- Review units 73-74 in *Basic Mathematics Simplified.*
- Apply the principles of geometric constructions to the work of the machinist by solving the Review Problems which follow.

REVIEW PROBLEMS

1. Bisect a straight line.

2. Divide a line into any number of equal parts.

3. Through a given point, draw a line parallel to a given line.

4. Draw a perpendicular from a point to a line.

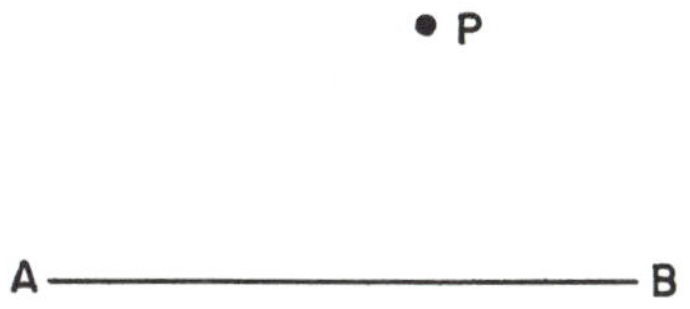

• P

A —————————————— B

5. Construct an angle equal to angle a.

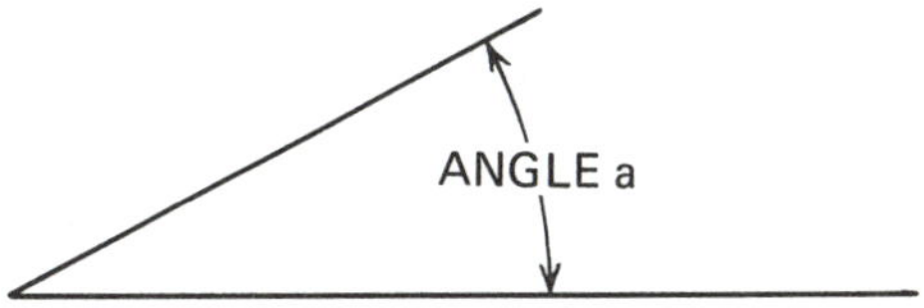

ANGLE a

6. Draw a circle through points A, B, and C.

POINT A •

• POINT C

POINT B •

7. Draw a line tangent to a circle at point P on the circumference.

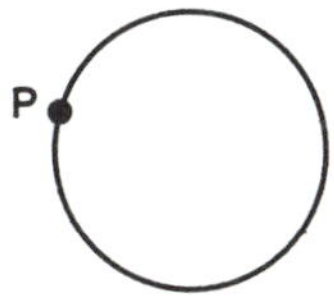

P

8. Draw a circle of given diameter tangent to two given circles.

9. Find the center of a circle from a given arc.

10. Draw a circle of given diameter tangent to any two intersecting straight lines.

11. Draw a circle of given diameter tangent to both a circle and a straight line.

12. Construct an angle of 45 degrees.

13. Construct an angle of 22 1/2 degrees.

14. Construct an angle of 30 degrees.

15. Construct an angle of 15 degrees.

Unit 54 SHOP PROBLEMS

BASIC PRINCIPLES OF PROBLEMS

- Review units 73-74 in *Basic Mathematics Simplified.*
- Apply the principles of geometric constructions to the work of the machinist by solving the Review Problems which follow.

REVIEW PROBLEMS

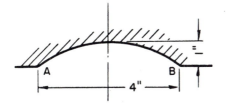

1. By construction, locate the center of the circular arc shown on the diagram and find the distance that A and B must be located from the center of a face plate if a piece of this shape is to be bored.

2. A piece of abrasive wheel is found to be exactly the shape shown here. Reproduce the curve and find the diameter of the wheel from which it was broken.

3. Two gears, one with a pitch diameter of 3 inches and the other, 4 inches, are spaced 5 inches on center. Lay out a 6-inch gear which will mesh with these two.

4. Lay out a circular plate as shown with 3 one-quarter-inch holes in the first circle; 4 three-eighth-inch holes in the second circle; and 6 one-half-inch holes in the third circle.

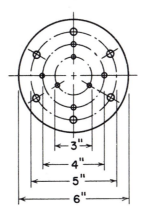

5. A 2-inch shank is required on the end of a piece of 4-inch round stock. Since the milling machines are in use, lay out the square on the end of the stock, so that the job can be done in a shaper. Would it be worthwhile to turn this piece on a lathe before shaping it?

6. By construction, lay out the center for a hole midway between two end holes of a drill jig. Use any center distance.

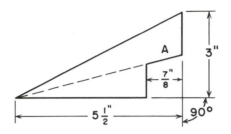

7. To layout the template shown in the illustration, it is necessary to bisect the angle to get the cut at A. Lay out the piece by construction.

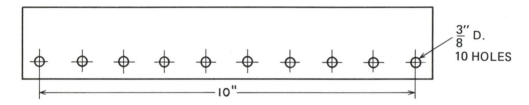

8. Ten equally spaced holes are punched along the edge of a piece of stock, with the centers of extreme holes 10 inches apart. Lay out holes by construction, as in the drawing.

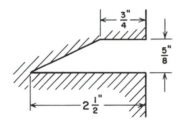

9. The drawing of the 5/8-inch thick gage is used to check the grinding angle on the blade of a power shear. Lay out a new gage with the same angle to be used on a blade 7/8 inch thick.

10. Lay out a gear drive as shown on the diagram, with gear A driving the other four gears. Use pitch diameters of A equal to 4 inches; B equal to 2 inches; C equal to 3 inches; D equal to 2 1/2 inches; E equal to 3 3/4 inches. Allow 1 inch between B-C, C-D, and D-E for clearance.

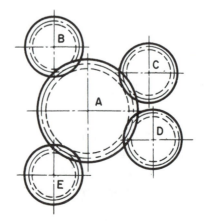

11. This diagram shows a brass tag. By construction, lay out a punch for blanking out tags like this. Use a piece of 2 1/2 inch round steel and work from the centerlines.

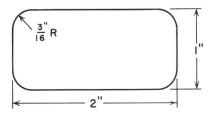

12. Lay out a shim to fit the bearing cap shown in the diagram.

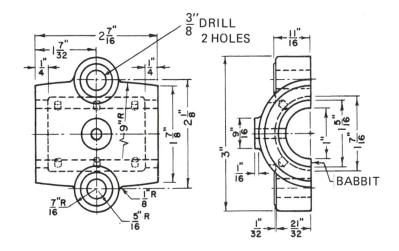

13. In laying out the drill jig, draw one centerline and then draw the other centerline vertical to the first at midpoint. Draw lines parallel to centerlines to locate holes. Check by swinging three arcs from the center hole and arcs through B and D from centers of A and C.

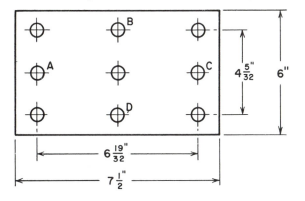

Unit 55 PRACTICAL APPLICATIONS OF GRAPHS AND CHARTS

BASIC PRINCIPLES OF GRAPHS AND CHARTS

- Study units 33-35 in *Basic Mathematics Simplified*.
- Apply the principles of graphs and charts to the work of the machinist by solving the Review Problems which follow.

REVIEW PROBLEMS

Graphs are used to show at a glance a large number of individual readings for the purpose of comparing, estimating unknown values, or solving problems. The graph, as illustrated, shows temperature readings from midnight to noon as given in the following table.

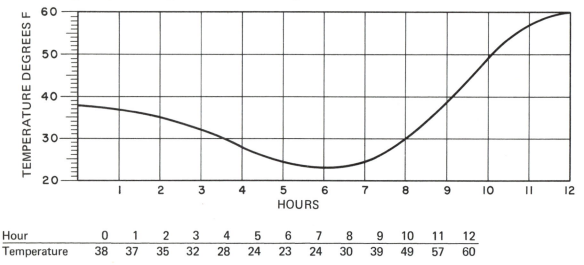

Hour	0	1	2	3	4	5	6	7	8	9	10	11	12
Temperature	38	37	35	32	28	24	23	24	30	39	49	57	60

To estimate the temperature at 8:30, draw a vertical line from a point midway between 8 o'clock and 9 o'clock intersecting the curve and project a line from the point of intersection horizontally to the temperature scale. This gives a reading of 34° as the temperature at 8:30.

1. Make a graph plotting units of production against weeks for a ten-week period using the following figures. _____

Weeks	1	2	3	4	5	6	7	8	9	10
Units	85	70	80	95	85	60	75	85	80	75

2. Find the average for 10 weeks and draw dotted line marked "average." _____

3. What weeks are above average? _____

4. What weeks are below average? _____

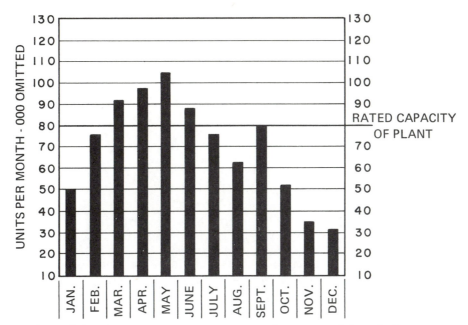

Some of the following statements are true and some are false. Indicate whether true or false, according to the graph shown, by using T and F after the statement.

5. Fewer units were shipped in January than any other month.   _____

6. More units were shipped in May than any other month.   _____

7. The graph shows continuous increase in the rate of production throughout the year.   _____

8. The plant was working above rated capacity half of the year.   _____

9. More units were shipped in May than in the last three months combined.   _____

10. The average for the four high months was above 90,000 units per month.   _____

11. For two thirds of the year the factory was running below rated capacity.   _____

12. The average throughout the year was above the rated capacity of the plant.   _____

13. The plant was running at less than 50% of rated capacity for one fourth of the year.   _____

14. The peak load came in the month of May.   _____

The accompanying figure is what is known as a sector diagram, or, as it is sometimes referred to, a pie chart. The sector diagram provides a convenient means of illustrating graphically the distribution of various items.

This particular diagram illustrates the distribution of the selling price of a certain article. Such a chart makes it possible to see at a glance just where the money goes and to appreciate the relative importance of each item.

15. Construct a sector diagram illustrating the distribution of the total expenditures of a machine company for one year: wages 40%, materials 25%, replacements 15%, light and power 3%, dividends 6%, interest and taxes 8%, miscellaneous 3%.

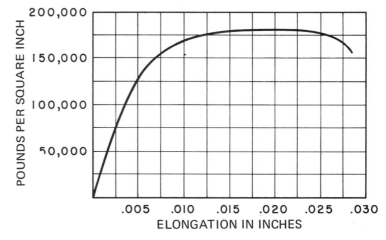

The preceding graph shows how the elongation of hard-drawn steel varies under tension according to the load.

16. What is the elongation at a 125,000-pound load? _____

17. What is the load required for .015-inch elongation? _____

18. What is the load required for .0025-inch elongation? _____

19. What is the elongation at a 175,000-pound load? _____

20. The point where the curve leaves the straight line is called the "yield point." At what load is the yield point of the specimen plotted? _____

21. A steel beam falling from rest falls through 4 feet in 1/2 second, 16 feet in 1 second, 36 feet in 1 1/2 second, 64 feet in 2 seconds, 100 feet in 2 1/2 seconds and 144 feet in 3 seconds. Plot using 1 square for 10 feet horizontal and 2 squares for 1 second vertical.

22. Find, from curve, how many seconds the steel beam would require to fall 80 feet. _____

23. Find the distance the steel beam would fall in 2 3/4 seconds. _____

24. In an experiment on the stretching of an iron rod the linear extension L in inches, for load W in pounds was as follows:

W	600	1100	1600	2100	2600	3100	3600	4100	4600	5100
L	.005	.009	.013	.018	.022	.027	.032	.037	.043	.050

Plot, choosing suitable distance for W horizontal and L vertical.

25. At what load does the yield point occur?

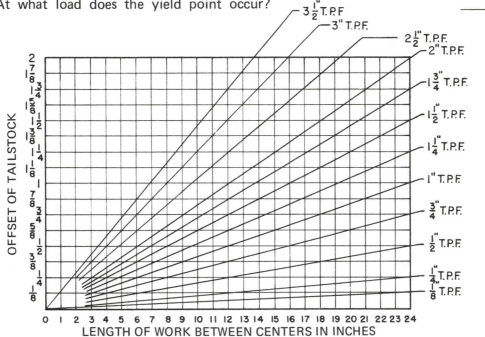

The preceding graph may be used for determining the amount to set over the tailstock of a lathe for turning a taper when the length of the work and the taper per inch is known. The horizontal lines represent the offset, the amount being shown by the column of dimensions at the left. The oblique lines represent taper per foot, the amount being marked on the line or at its extreme right.

Using the preceding graph, determine the missing factor for turning each of the tapers described below.

	Length of Work	Taper per Foot	Offset
26.	10 inches	5/8 inch	_____
27.	22 inches	7/8 inch	_____
28.	8 inches	3/4 inch	_____
29.	6 inches	1 3/4 inch	_____
30.	14 inches	_____	5/8 inch
31.	9 inches	_____	1 1/4 inch
32.	4 inches	_____	5/8 inch
33.	_____	2 inches	3/8 inch
34.	_____	3/8 inch	1/4 inch
35.	_____	1 1/2 inches	1 1/8 inches

Unit 56 PLOTTING EQUATIONS

BASIC PRINCIPLES OF DEVELOPING GRAPHS AND CHARTS

- Study unit 34 in *Basic Mathematics Simplified.*

- Apply the principles for developing graphs and charts to the work of the machinist by solving the Review Problems which follow.

REVIEW PROBLEMS

The accompanying graph shows the equation X + Y = 1 as plotted from values x = +4 to X = -4.

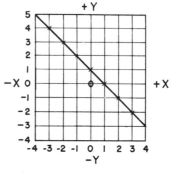

Using the graph, answer the following:

1. a. x = 4   y = _____   d. x = 0   y = _____

    b. x = 3   y = _____   e. x = -1   y = _____

    c. x = 1   y = _____   f. x = -4   y = _____

2. Plot x + y = 2 using x = -6, -5, -4, -3, -2, -1, 0, 1, 2, 3, 4, 5, 6.   _____
    Draw a line through the points plotted. Is this a curved or straight line?

3. Plot the curve for x^2 = y using values of x from -10 to +10. From   _____
    the curve read the following values: _____

    a. Square of 4 1/2, -3 1/2, 3 3/4.   _____

    b. Square root of 55, 70, 30.   _____
                                                                              _____
                                                                              _____

4. Using the formula C = πd for circumference of circle, plot curve using
    diameters from 0 to 10 as abscissas and circumferences as ordinates.

5. Using formula A = πr^2 for area of circle, plot curve using radii from
    0 to 6 as abscissas and area as ordinates.

6. The circular pitch of a gear is found by dividing 3.1416 by the diam-
    etral pitch.   Plot, using circular pitch from 1 inch to 6 inches as
    abscissas and the corresponding diametral pitch as ordinates. Make
    the ordinate scale twice that of abscissa.

7. From the graph in the preceding problem, find the circular pitch for   _____
    a 2 1/2 diametral pitch.

8. Find the circular pitch for 4 1/2 diametral pitch.   _____

9. Find the diametral pitch for 1-inch circular pitch.   _____

Unit 57 NATURAL FUNCTIONS

BASIC PRINCIPLES OF TRIGONOMETRY

- Study units 76-78 in *Basic Mathematics Simplified* for the principles of trigonometry.
- Apply the principles of trigonometry to the work of the machinist by solving the Review Problems which follow.

REVIEW PROBLEMS

Note: Use Trigonometric tables (Natural Functions) found in the textbook.

1. Find the value of each function (use tables):

   a. Sine 64 degrees   = _____

   b. Sine 86 degrees 6 minutes   = _____

   c. Cosine 41 degrees 22 minutes   = _____

   d. Tangent 26 degrees 14 minutes   = _____

   e. Cosine 52 degrees 58 minutes   = _____

   f. Tangent 72 degrees 7 minutes   = _____

2. Find the angle corresponding to function given:

   a. Sine   = .42262   Angle = _____

   b. Tangent = .38386   Angle = _____

   c. Cosine = .73135   Angle = _____

   d. Tangent = 2.05030   Angle = _____

   e. Sine   = .77715   Angle = _____

   f. Cosine = .10453   Angle = _____

3. Find the value of each function:

   a. Sine 26.25 degrees   = _____

   b. Cosine 81.36 degrees   = _____

   c. Tangent 61.08 degrees   = _____

   d. Cosine 7.92 degrees   = _____

   e. Sine 89.66 degrees   = _____

   f. Tangent 22.46 degrees   = _____

Find the function of the given angles.

4. Sine 21 degrees 13 minutes 17 seconds   _____

5. Sine 21 degrees 13 minutes 52 seconds   _____

6. Tangent 14 degrees 18 minutes 27 seconds   _____

7. Cotangent 56 degrees 49 minutes 52 seconds   _____

8. Cosine 10 degrees 13 minutes 16 seconds   _____

9. Sine 82 degrees 43 minutes 42 seconds   _____

10. Cotangent 61 degrees 7 minutes 14 seconds   _____

11. Cosine 29 degrees 13 minutes 42 seconds   _____

12. Tangent 28 degrees 29 minutes 26 seconds   _____

13. Cotangent 66 degrees 22.6 minutes   _____

Find the angle; the function is given.

14. Sine A = .64856   _____

15. Tangent A = 1.8954   _____

16. Cotangent A = .76583   _____

17. Cosine A = .23542   _____

18. Tangent A = .77656   _____

19. Cotangent A = 1.8563   _____

20. Sine A = .02534   _____

21. Tangent A = 2.6003   _____

22. Tangent A = .47568   _____

23. Cotangent A = .58998   _____

Unit 58 *TYPICAL TRIGONOMETRIC SOLUTIONS*

BASIC PRINCIPLES OF TRIGONOMETRY

- Study units 76-78 in *Basic Mathematics Simplified.*
- Apply the principles of trigonometry to the work of the machinist by solving the Review Problems which follow.

REVIEW PROBLEMS

1. What function is used to find the side X of the right-angle triangle shown in the illustration? _____

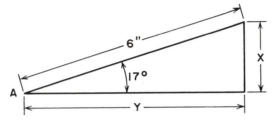

2. Solve for the value of X. _____
3. What function is used to find side Y? _____
4. Solve for the value of Y. _____
5. With angle A changed to 42 degrees, find X. _____
6. With angle A changed to 42 degrees, find Y. _____

   In triangle ABC substitute the following values and solve.

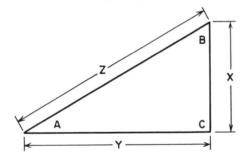

7. Z = 3 inches   A = 37 degrees   Find X. _____
8. Z = 6 inches   A = 22 degrees 40 minutes   Find Y. _____
9. Two holes are to be located in a plate as shown. After boring hole A the table carrying the plate is moved horizontally the distance Y and vertically the distance X in order to locate hole B. Find the distances X and Y. _____
_____

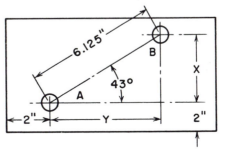

Changing the distances on the diagram as listed, solve the following:

10. AB = 14 inches   angle A   = 56 degrees   Find X and Y.   _____

                                                                            _____

11. AB = 14 inches   angle A   = 2 degrees 41 minutes.   Find X   _____
     and Y.
                                                                            _____

12. AB = 7 1/2 inches   angle A= 89 degrees 1 minute. Find X and Y.   _____

                                                                            _____

13. AB = 12 1/4 inches angle B = 72 degrees   Find X and Y.   _____

                                                                            _____

14. AB = 4.127 inches   angle B= 27 degrees   Find X and Y.   _____

                                                                            _____

Six holes are spaced evenly around a 2-inch diameter circle, figure 1.
To find the distance AB, solve the following problems.

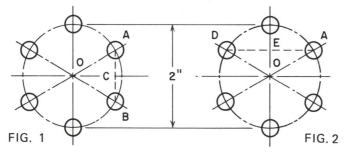

FIG. 1   FIG. 2

15. What is the value of angle AOB? Of angle AOC?   _____

                                                                      _____

16. What is the length of radius OA?   _____

17. In the triangle AOC, the hypotenuse OA and the angle at O are   _____
     known. What function will be used to find AC?

18. Solve for AC.   _____

19. What is the length of AB?   _____

20. In order to check the accuracy of the work after boring the holes,   _____
     measure across alternate holes A and D in figure 2. By the use of
     trigonometry, find what measurement AD should be.

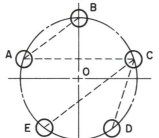

21. Five holes are to be equally spaced about a circle. With a radius OB   _____
     equal to 1 inch, find the distance between centers of holes A and B.

22. With radius of 1 inch, AC equals _____

23. With radius of 1 1/4 inches, DC equals _____

24. With radius of 1 1/4 inches, EC equals _____

25. With radius of 2.146 inches, AB equals _____

26. With radius of 2.146 inches, CE equals _____

27. With AB equal to 2 inches, the radius equals _____

28. With AC equal to 3 inches, the diameter equals _____

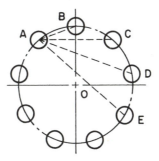

29. Nine holes are equally spaced around a 6-inch diameter circle, as shown. Find the distance between centers of holes A and B. _____

30. Find the distance between the centers of holes A and C. _____

31. Find the distance between the centers of holes A and D. _____

32. Find the distance between the centers of holes A and E. _____

33. Find the distance between centers of adjacent holes when 26 holes are spaced around a circle 6 feet in diameter. _____

34. Find the distance between centers of alternate holes when 17 holes are spaced around a circle with an 18-inch radius. _____

Unit 59 TAPERS AND WEDGES

BASIC PRINCIPLES OF TRIGONOMETRY

- Review unit 78 in *Basic Mathematics Simplified.*

- Apply the principles of trigonometry to the work of the machinist by solving the Review Problems which follow.

REVIEW PROBLEMS

Note: To find angle O in the wedge shown when triangle ABD is not a right triangle, draw AC perpendicular to (and bisecting) the base BD. Proceed then as indicated in the following problems:

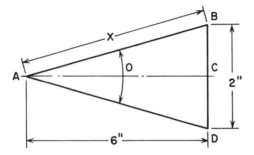

1. In triangle ABC, what length is the side opposite angle A? The adjacent side? _____

2. What function is used to find angle BAC? _____

3. Set up a trigonometry equation and find the value of angle BAC. _____

4. What is the value of O? _____

5. What function may be used to find length X? _____

6. Find length X by trigonometry. _____

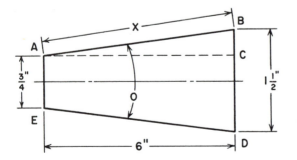

Note: In the sketch shown, to find the included angle, line AC is drawn parallel to the centerline giving the right triangle ABC.

7. Considering the angle at A in the right triangle ABC what is the length of the opposite side? The adjacent side? _____ _____

8. What function will be used to find angle BAC? _____

118

9. What is the value of angle BAC?   _____

10. What is the value of O?   _____

11. Find the length of side x.   _____

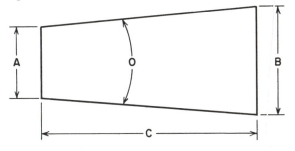

Use the diagram to find the included angle O for tapers of the dimensions given in inches in the following problems.

12. A = 1 1/4   B = 2 1/2   C = 5   _____

13. A = 3 1/8   B = 3 1/4   C = 4   _____

14. A = 1.250   B = 1.914   C = 2 1/4   _____

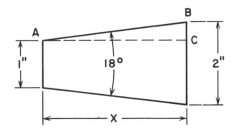

In the taper shown:

15. What is the value of angle BAC?   _____

16. What length is BC?   _____

17. What is the diameter of end X?   _____

In the taper shown:

18. What is the value of angle BAC?   _____

19. What is the length of BC?   _____

20. Find the length X.   _____

21. Find the length of side AB.   _____

22. Large end equals 6 1/2 inches   Small end equals 5 1/8 inches   _____
     Angle BAC equals 8 degrees   Find X.

Unit 60 HELIX ANGLES

BASIC PRINCIPLES OF TRIGONOMETRY

- Study unit 78 in *Basic Mathematics Simplified.*
- Apply the principles of trigonometry to the work of the machinist by solving the Review Problems which follow.

REVIEW PROBLEMS

Note: The curved line which the point of a tool makes on the surface of a cylinder in cutting a thread is a *helix.* The horizontal distance advanced by the helix in making a complete revolution is called the *lead* of the screw. If one turn of the helix could be unwrapped from the surface of the cylinder it would form the hypotenuse AC of the right triangle ABC, in which the side AB is equal to the lead and the side BC is equal to the circumference. The angle BCA is the helix angle.

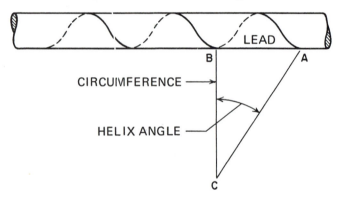

In cutting straight screw threads on a lathe, the tool travels parallel to the centerline of the work, while the work rotates. As the tool cuts, it cuts a helical groove on the work.

The amount of feed per revolution of the work determines the lead of the screw thread cut and is achieved by a combination of gears connecting the spindle and lead screw of the lathe.

The helix angle can be determined by the ratio formula in trigonometry:

$$\text{tangent of angle} = \frac{\text{opposite side}}{\text{adjacent side}} \qquad \frac{\text{tangent of}}{\text{helix angle}} = \frac{\text{lead}}{\text{circumference}}$$

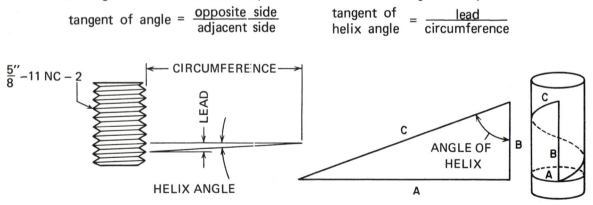

**HELIX ANGLE
PLUS CLEARANCE**

This provides a method for figuring the helix angle which must be known in order to grind the proper clearance on the threading tool and in setting the cutter on the thread milling machine.

Find the helix angle of the following threads, using the pitch diameter of National Form Threads. Answers should be correct to the nearest minute.

1. 1 1/2 inch — 4 1/2 _____

2. 3 inch — 2 1/2 _____

3. 5 inch — 2 1/2 _____

4. 3 5/16 inch — 3 _____

Find the helix angle of the following National Coarse Threads, using the pitch diameter. Give answers correct to nearest minute.

5. 1/4 inch — 20 _____

6. 3/4 inch — 10 _____

7. 5/16 inch — 18 _____

8. 1/2 inch — 13 _____

9. 3/8 inch — 16 _____

10. 3/8 inch — 16
  double thread _____

In order to grind the proper clearance on a threading tool it is necessary to know the helix angle of the thread. Find the helix angle of the following square threads, using outside diameter. Give answers correct to nearest minute.

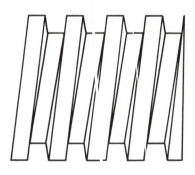

11. 2 inch diameter; 8 threads per inch _____

12. 3 1/4 inch diameter; 5 threads per inch _____

Find helix angle for square threads, using minor diameter. Give answers correct to nearest minute.

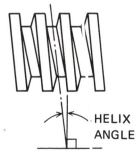

**HELIX
ANGLE**

13. 2 inch diameter; 8 threads per inch _____

14. 3 1/4 inch diameter; 5 threads per inch _____

Note: The helix for drills, cutters, and gears is similar to the helix for screw threads. The horizontal distance advanced by the helix in making a complete revolution is called the *lead.* The side BC of triangle ABC is equal to the circumference and hypotenuse AC is the helix. Angle *BAC* is the helix angle.

Rule: The tangent of the helix angle is equal to the circumference divided by the lead.

$$\text{tangent helix angle} = \frac{\text{circumference}}{\text{lead}} \quad \text{or} \quad \frac{3.1416 \times \text{diameter}}{\text{lead}}$$

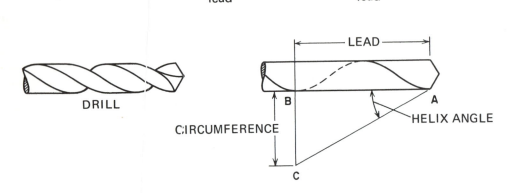

DRILL

Compare the location of the helix angle shown on page 120 with the location of the helix angle shown on this page. In order to understand this difference, imagine that a triangle of the same slope as shown (a) is cut out of paper and wrapped around a rod (b). The helix curve shown in (c) results.

If this curve represents a helix of a screw thread, the helix angle will be 70 degrees. If this curve represents the helix of a twist drill, a helical gear, or a cutter, then the helix angle will be 20 degrees.

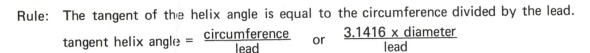

(a)   (b)   (c)

To find the cutter angle for setting a milling cutter for a drill 1 1/2 inches in diameter with a lead of 9 inches, construct a right triangle, using the lead as one leg, and proceed as follows:

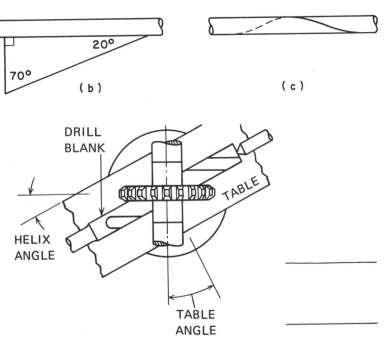

15. What is the circumference of the drill?   (Mark this on triangle.)   _____

16. What function will be used to find the helix angle?   _____

17. What is the value of the helix angle?   _____

18. A 7/8-inch drill has a lead of 5 1/4 inches.   Find the helix angle.   _____

19. A 25/32-inch drill has a helix angle of 27 1/2 degrees.   Find the lead.   _____

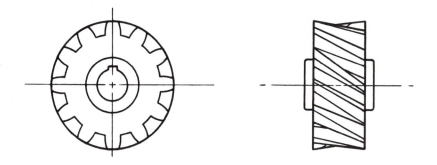

20. A helical gear with 3-inch pitch diameter has a lead of 6.134 inches. What is the angle of helix?   _____

    Find the helix angle of the following gears:

21. Pitch diameter =   4.695 inches,   Lead   =   6.567 inches   _____

22. Pitch diameter = 12.543 inches,   Lead   = 88.512 inches   _____

23. Pitch diameter =   8.531 inches,   Lead   = 23.315 inches   _____

    Find the lead of the following gears:

24. Pitch diameter =   2.771 inches,   Helix angle = 61 degrees   _____

25. Pitch diameter = 6.765 inches, Helix angle = 43 degrees 29 minutes   _____

Unit 61 MEASURING DOVETAILS

BASIC PRINCIPLES APPLIED TO MEASURING DOVETAILS

- Review units 76-78 in *Basic Mathematics Simplified.*

- Apply the principles of trigonometry to the work of the machinist by solving the Review Problems which follow.

REVIEW PROBLEMS

A common way to measure dovetails accurately is to 'mike' over a pair of plugs, as shown in A, for distance X. In order to have this measurement of any value, it is necessary to first find what the distance X should be. To do this, first find Y. If lines BD and BC are drawn to the tangent points, as in B, two equal right angle triangles are obtained. Side AC plus 1/2 the diameter of the plug is equal to Y. Dimension X then, is equal to the basic dimension, 3.1416 inches in this case, plus 2Y.

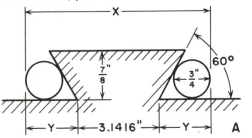 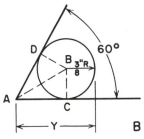

1. What is the value of angle BAC? of side BC? _____ _____

2. Find the value of side AC. _____

3. What is the length Y? _____

4. What is the length over plugs (X)? _____

5. If 1/2-inch plugs instead of 3/4-inch plugs are used, what is the value of X? _____

6. Find the value of X, using 5/8-inch plugs. _____

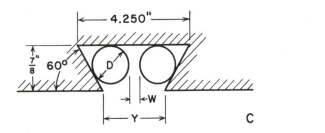 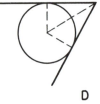

Make a diagram similar to D for each problem.

7. Find W, using 1/2-inch plugs. _____

8. Find W, using 3/8-inch plugs. _____

124

9. Find the value of Y.

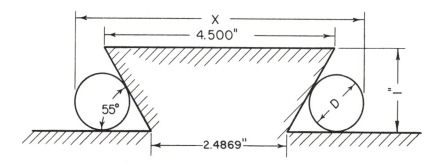

10. Find X, using 3/4-inch plugs.

11. Find X, using 1/2-inch plugs.

12. Find X, using 15/16-inch plugs.

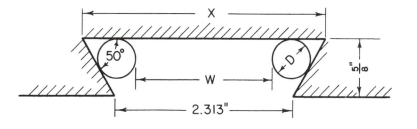

13. Find W, using 3/8-inch plugs.

14. Find W, using 1/2-inch plugs.

15. Find the value of X.

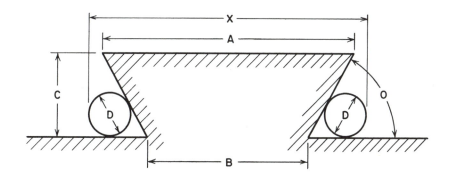

Solve the following for an outside dovetail, using the diagram.

16. B = 2.149 D = 3/4 O = 60 degrees   Find X.

17. A = 3.125 C = 3/4 O = 60 degrees D = 1/2   Find X.

18. X = 3.219 O = 60 degrees   D = 1/2   Find B.

19. An internal dovetail slide is cut on an angle of 45 degrees, as shown in the diagram. B equals 4 1/4 inches and, at its widest part, the dovetail is 3 inches. What are height C and dimension Y, if the plugs are .4375 inch diameter?

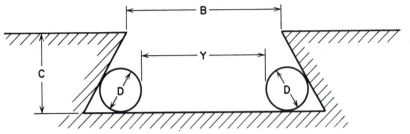

20. A drawing of an internal and an external dovetail slide is shown. The plugs are 7/8 inches in diameter. What are dimensions C, X, and Y?

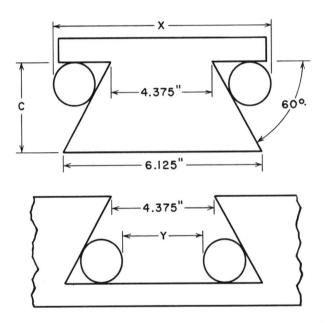

21. If in the preceding example, the angle had been cut 58 degrees 45 minutes instead of 60 degrees, what difference would it make in X and Y?

Unit 62 MEASURING THREADS

BASIC PRINCIPLES APPLIED TO MEASURING THREADS

- Review units 76-78 in *Basic Mathematics Simplified.*
- Apply the principles of trigonometry to the work of the machinist by solving the Review Problems which follow.

REVIEW PROBLEMS

The "three wire" method of measuring the pitch diameter of screws is recommended by the Bureau of Standards as the best means of securing uniformity. The best size of wire is that which touches the thread at the pitch line (the middle of the sloping sides).

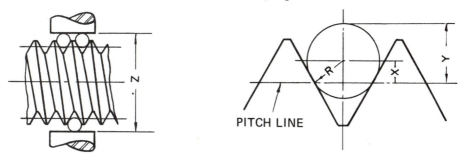

To find the correct measurement over wires for 1/2-inch — 13 National Coarse thread using a best wire diameter of .04441, proceed as follows:

1. Find length X, using the given data. _____

2. What is the distance Y? _____

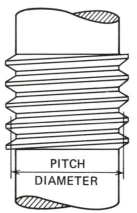

3. What is the pitch diameter of a 1/2-inch — 13 National Coarse thread? _____

4. What is the measurement over wires (Z)? _____

5. Find the measurement over wires for a 3/8-inch — 16 National Coarse thread, using .03608 best wire. _____

6. Find the measurement over wires for a 3/4-inch — 16 National Fine thread, using .03608 best wire. _____

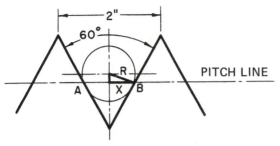

FINDING THE "BEST WIRE SIZE"

The best wire for measuring threads is a wire that touches the side of the thread at the pitch line. The size of this wire may be found in the following manner for any thread, if the pitch and the angle are known.

7. In the sketch, what is the length of AB?   _____

8. What is length X in the small triangle?   _____

9. What is the value of angle B in this triangle?   _____

10. Find the length of hypotenuse R.   _____

11. What is the diameter of the best wire?   _____

Find the size of best wire to be used in measuring the following threads:

12. V thread, 3 threads per inch.   _____

13. V thread, 9 threads per inch.   _____

14. American National, 3 threads per inch.   _____

15. American National, 5 threads per inch.   _____

Find the measurement over wires for the following threads. For the best wire sizes, refer to handbook.

16. 1/4-inch — 28 National Fine thread.   _____

17. 5/16-inch — 18 National Coarse thread.   _____

18. 1-inch — 14 National Extra Fine thread.   _____

Unit 63 MEASURING ANGLE CUTS

BASIC PRINCIPLES APPLIED TO MEASURING ANGLE CUTS

- Review units 76-78 in *Basic Mathematics Simplified.*

- Apply the principles of trigonometry to the work of the machinist by solving the Review Problems which follow.

REVIEW PROBLEMS

To accurately measure a cut, as shown, the size of a plug which will be flush with the top surface is calculated. The plug is turned to size and then used to test the accuracy of the cut.

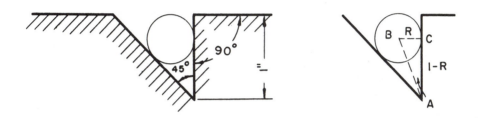

Find the size plug to use in the cut shown in the illustration as follows:

1. What is the value of angle A?   _____

2. Knowing the value of angle A and that the opposite side is R and the adjacent side (1-R), what function can be used to solve for R?   _____

3. What is the value of R?   _____

4. What is the diameter of the plug?   _____

5. What is the diameter of the plug, if the angle is 60 degrees instead of 45 degrees?   _____

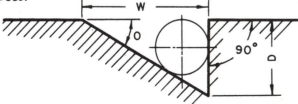

Find the size of a plug to be used in the following problems, using the diagram:

6. D = 2 inches   O = 30 degrees   _____

7. D = 1 inch   O = 60 degrees   _____

8. D = 3/4 inch   O = 24 degrees   _____

9. D = 1 1/4 inches   O = 15 degrees 20 minutes   _____

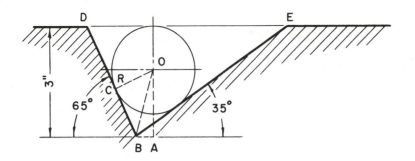

To find the diameter of a plug to measure cut shown in the preceding illustration proceed as follows:

10. What are the values of angles DBE, OBE, OBA, and BOA?

    _____

    _____   _____   _____

11. Using triangle OBA with side OA equal to 3-R and knowing angle BOA, solve for side OB in terms of R.

    _____

12. Using triangle OCB with the value of OB in terms of R as found, OC equal to R, and angle COB known, solve for the value of R.

13. What is the diameter of the plug?

    _____

    Solve for the diameter of the plug in the following problems, using the accompanying diagram:

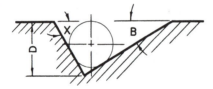

14. D = 2 inches   X = 30 degrees   B = 60 degrees

    _____

15. D = 3 inches   X = 70 degrees   B = 10 degrees

    _____

    Solve for the size of plug in the following problems, using the accompanying diagram:

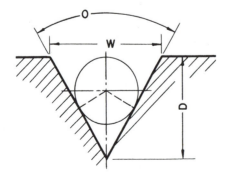

16. D = 2 inches   O = 60 degrees

    _____

17. W = 4 inches   O = 60 degrees

    _____

Unit 64 MEASURING ACME THREADS

BASIC PRINCIPLES APPLIED TO MEASURING ACME THREADS

- Review units 76-78 in *Basic Mathematics Simplified.*

- Apply the principles of trigonometry to the work of the machinist by solving the Review Problems which follow.

REVIEW PROBLEMS

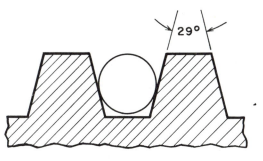

1. Find the diameter of the wire that will fit flush with the top of the threads of a 1/4-inch pitch Acme tap. _____

2. Find the diameter of a wire that will fit flush with the top of an Acme Thread which has 5 1/2 threads per inch. _____

A sketch of the cross section of a Worm Thread is shown, together with a table giving its important properties. The Worm Thread differs from the Acme in several features, although like the Acme, it has the 29 degree angle.

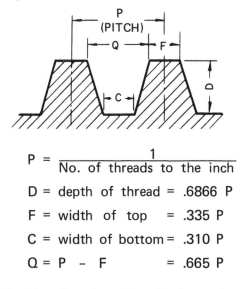

$$P = \frac{1}{\text{No. of threads to the inch}}$$

D = depth of thread = .6866 P

F = width of top   = .335 P

C = width of bottom = .310 P

Q = P – F   = .665 P

3. Work out a formula for the diameter of a wire for gaging a Worm Thread. The formula should express the diameter of the wire in terms of pitch. _____

4. Find the diameter of the wire that will fit flush with the top of the threads on a Worm that has five threads to the inch; 4 1/2 threads to the inch; 10 threads to the inch.

5. A wire that had the correct diameter for gaging an Acme Tap with 3 1/2 threads to the inch was used by mistake to gage a Worm Thread of the same pitch. How did this wire set in the groove of the Worm Thread? Did it come above or below the top of the threads and how much?

6. What pitch Acme thread would a .0527 inch diameter wire be used to gage?

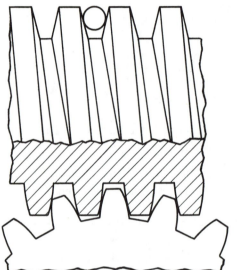

7. A wire .0286 inch in diameter sets in a groove of a Worm thread just flush with the top. What is the pitch of the Worm?

Unit 65 MEASURING ANGLES WITH SINE BAR

BASIC PRINCIPLES OF MEASURING ANGLES

- Review units 76-78 in *Basic Mathematics Simplified* for the principles of measuring angles with a sine bar.

- Apply the principles of trigonometry to the work of the machinist by solving the Review Problems which follow.

REVIEW PROBLEMS

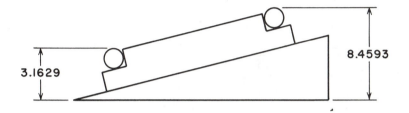

1. When a sine bar is in position for measuring a certain angle, the distances from the plate to the disk are found to be 3.1629 inches and 8.4593 inches respectively. Find the angle to the nearest second. Unless otherwise specified, consider a sine bar as 10 inches between centers.

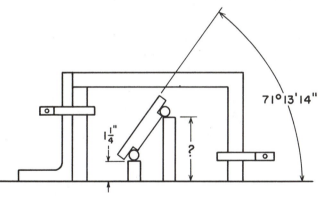

2. A toolmaker wants to lay off an angle of 71 degrees 13 minutes 14 seconds with the edge of a flat rectangular plate. He makes a setup similar to the one shown in the diagram. What should he make the measurement to the other button?

   Note: When measuring angles which cannot be conveniently placed with one side parallel to the surface plate, two operations are necessary. The angle may be considered as divided into two parts by an imaginary line through the vertex, parallel to the plate.

3. When a sine bar is placed along one side of an angle, the measurements to the buttons are 2.1672 inches and 4.8634 inches, respectively, and when placed along the other side, the measurements are 5.6729 inches and 9.2173 inches. Find the angle.

Unit 66 MEASURING ANGLES (DISK METHOD)

BASIC PRINCIPLES OF DISK METHOD

- Review units 76-78 in *Basic Mathematics Simplified.*

- Apply the principles of trigonometry to the work of the machinist by solving the Review Problems which follow.

REVIEW PROBLEMS

1. Two disks, 1 1/4 inches and 1 3/4 inches in diameter, respectively, are placed in contact with each other and straight edges placed tangent to them. What is the included angle between the straight edges? _____

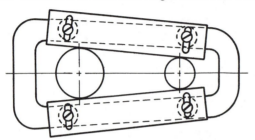

2. How far apart on centers are two standard reference disks 1 inch and 2 inches in diameter, respectively, placed to lay out an angle of 9 degrees 27 minutes? _____

3. Two disks, one 7/8 inch and the other 2 1/4 inches in diameter, are used to measure a taper. The distance between disk centers is 3 7/8 inches. What is the rate of taper per foot? _____

4. A piece of work tapers at the rate of 7/8 inch per foot. If the included angle of the taper is measured by two disks whose diameters are 9/16 inch and 1 3/16 inches, respectively, what is the distance between centers? _____

5. The smaller of two disks used to measure an angle of 4 degrees 21 minutes is 1 1/4 inches in diameter. What is the diameter of the larger disk, if they are placed 2 7/8 inches on centers as shown? _____

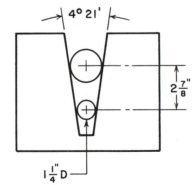

6. The center distance between two disks used to lay out a taper of 13/16 inch per foot is 2.767 inches. The larger of the two disks is 1.875 inches in diameter; what is the diameter of the smaller disk? _____

Unit 67 MISCELLANEOUS PROBLEMS

BASIC PRINCIPLES OF TRIGONOMETRY

- Review units 76-78 in *Basic Mathematics Simplified* for the principles of trigonometry.

- Apply the principles of trigonometry to the work of the machinist by solving the Review Problems which follow.

REVIEW PROBLEMS

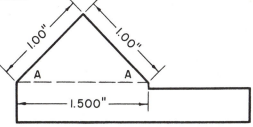

1. A steel block is to be finished to the dimensions shown in the drawing. Determine angle A at which to plane the sloping surfaces.   _____

2. The distance across the flats of a hexagonal nut is 1 1/4 inches. Determine the distance across the corners and the width of the flats.   _____

3. Find the depth of a V thread of 1/8-inch pitch.   _____

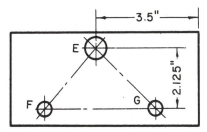

4. The layout for locating pins in a plate is shown.   Hole E is 2 1/8 inches distant from the centerline of holes F and G. Centerlines FE and EG forming 50 degrees and 40 degrees respectively, with line FG. Find distances EF, FG, EG, and the distance from the end of the plate to hole G.   _____

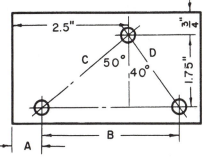

5. In the illustrated jig-plate, three holes must be located to the exact dimensions.   What are the distances A, B, C, and D required by the toolmaker?   _____

6. The ways on a sliding table are to be milled at 55 degrees, as shown. How far will the dovetail cutter be moved to cut a full depth?

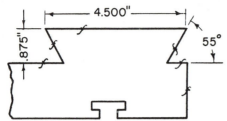

7. A bushing is to be bored, as illustrated. At what angle with the centerline of the piece will the compound rest be set to bore the tapered hole?

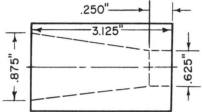

8. At what angle should the compound rest be set to turn the tapered portion of the end of the shaft, as shown in the sketch?

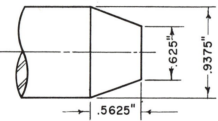

9. What is dimension D, in the dovetail shown, if two pieces of 5/8-inch drill rod are used to check the measurement after milling?

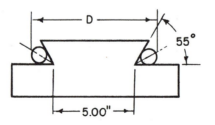

10. Two pieces of 3/8-inch drill rod are used to measure the distance across the machine part. The angles are 90 degrees and the faces are parallel. What is the micrometer reading across the plugs when the piece is finished to size?

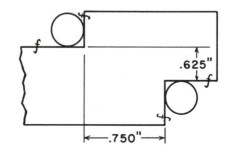

11. The lathe tool, as illustrated, is ground for cutting a V thread. If the clearance is 15 degrees, what is the included angle XYZ in the plane AB, perpendicular to CD?

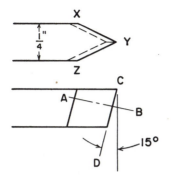

12. Determine the distance, center-to-center, of the 8 holes equally spaced on a 9-inch diameter circle, as shown in the sketch.

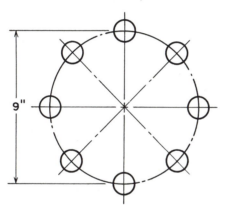

13. Five holes are to be equally spaced around a circle. They are **4.70** inches apart, center-to-center. Determine the diameter of the circle.

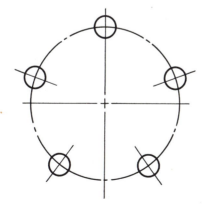

14. The layout for a jig plate calls for 5 holes, equally spaced on a 7 1/2-inch diameter circle. What is the exact distance of these holes, center-to-center? See accompanying sketch.

15. Find the center distances between alternate holes in the preceding problem, to provide a check on this job for the inspector.

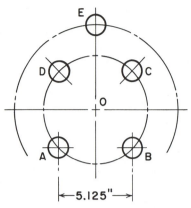

16. The jig plate layout, as illustrated, calls for four holes on the 6-inch diameter circle O. Hole E on a 7 1/2-inch diameter circle is equidistant from D and C. Holes A and B are 5 1/8 inches apart and distance AD = DC = CB. Find center distance AD, DE, and AC for checking the work.

17. Using three wires (.095-inch diameter drill rod), calculate the micrometer reading for a full size V thread, 1 inch in diameter, 8 threads per inch.

18. Using the same wires, find the measurement reading on a micrometer for a National Coarse thread 1 inch in diameter, 8 threads per inch.

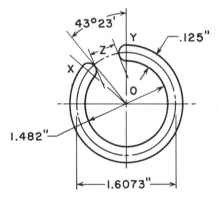

19. Using the layout of a circular slot as shown in the sketch find the included angle x o y, and the distance z for checking the slot after milling.

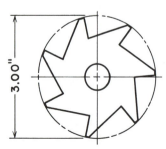

20. The milling cutter, as illustrated, measuring 3 inches in diameter has seven teeth. Find the exact measurement across the two teeth most nearly opposite.

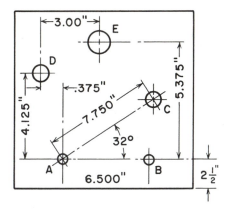

21. The plate layout, as illustrated, shows five holes; A and B are 1 inch in diameter, D and C are 1 1/8 inches in diameter. What should the dial reading be on a vertical milling machine, or the necessary stop gage be on a jig boring machine, to bore hole C using hole A as a starting point?

22. What should the vernier reading be across two plug gages, to check the distance D to C, also E to C?

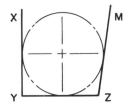

23. In the accompanying diagram, angle Y is a right angle and YZ equals 4 inches. Angle YZM is 105 degrees. What diameter plug gage will just touch all three sides?

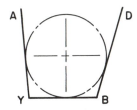

24. The angle Y, as shown in the diagram, is 95 degrees and YB is 4.5 inches. Angle YBD is 105 degrees. What diameter circle will be tangent to all three sides?

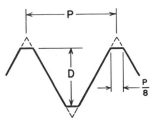

25. The American National thread has a flat at the top and bottom equal to 1/8 the pitch, as shown in the sketch. What is the depth of a 1-inch pitch American National thread?

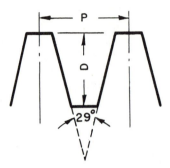

26. The Acme thread has a depth of 1/2 the pitch plus .010 inch. Find _____ the length of slope of a 1-inch thread.

27. The flat at the top of the Acme thread in the preceding problem is _____ equal to .3707 pitch. Find the thread thickness at its root.

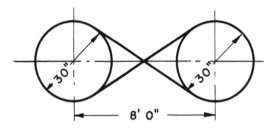

28. Find the exact length of the belt, as shown on the sketch. _____

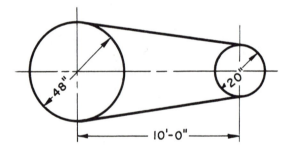

29. What is the exact length of the belt shown in the sketch? _____

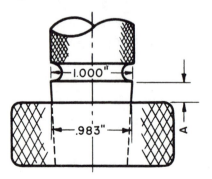

30. The ring gage, as illustrated, is tapered 1 1/2 inches per foot. The _____ diameter at the large end is .983 inch. The plug is 1-inch diameter at the large end. Find the distance "A."

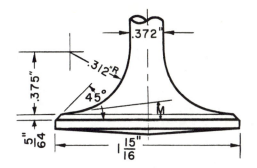

31. Find angle M on the illustrated valve head.   _____

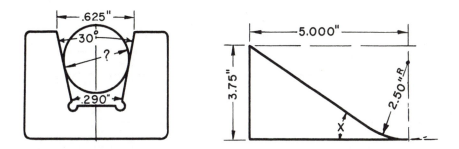

32. Find the size of a plug gage that will come even with the top of the   _____
     template as illustrated.

33. Find angle X on the triangular template, as illustrated.   _____

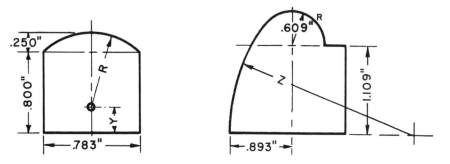

34. In making a punch and die radiused slope as shown, it is necessary to   _____
     know radius R and distance Y for checking.   Find Y and R.

35. What is radius Z of the curve in the illustrated template?   _____

Unit 68 FUNCTIONS OF ANGLES

BASIC PRINCIPLES OF OBLIQUE TRIANGLES

- Study unit 79 in *Basic Mathematics Simplified.*
- Apply the principles of oblique triangles to the work of the machinist by solving the Review Problems which follow.

REVIEW PROBLEMS

The following table shows the sign of each function in each quadrant.

Function	1st Quad.	2nd Quad.	3rd Quad.	4th Quad.
Sin.	+	+	−	−
Cos.	+	−	−	+
Tan.	+	−	+	−
Cot.	+	−	+	−

Look up the sine, cosine, tangent and cotangent of the following:

1. 127 degrees _____

2. 149 degrees 18 minutes _____

3. 218 degrees 41 minutes _____

4. 98 degrees 21 minutes 47 seconds _____

5. 328 degrees 42 minutes 51 seconds _____

6. 142 degrees 7 minutes 42 seconds _____

7. 298 degrees 41 minutes 7 seconds _____

8. 171 degrees 14 minutes 27 seconds _____

9. 164 degrees 18 minutes 51 seconds _____

Find the angles whose functions are as follows; find two values of A for each example.

10. .15931 = sin A _____

11. .31690 = cot A _____

12. .91793 = cos A _____

13. .37143 = tan A _____

Unit 69 LAWS OF SINES AND COSINES

BASIC PRINCIPLES OF TRIGONOMETRY

- Review unit 79 in *Basic Mathematics Simplified* for the Laws of Sines and Cosines.
- Apply the Laws of Sines and Cosines to the work of the machinist by solving the Review Problems which follow.

REVIEW PROBLEMS

Law of Sines

The sides of a triangle are to each other as the sines of the opposite angles. This rule is known as the law of sines.

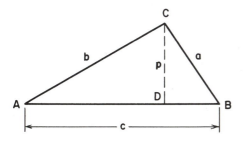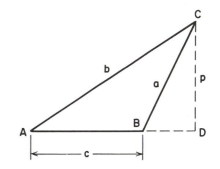

A convenient way of expressing the preceding rule is as follows:

$$\frac{a}{\sin A} = \frac{b}{\sin B} = \frac{c}{\sin C}$$

Law of Cosines

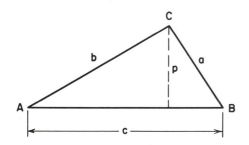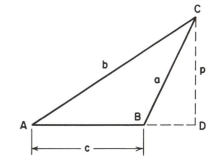

The law of cosines is expressed in the following formulas:

$$a = \sqrt{b^2 + c^2 - 2bc \, \cos A}$$

$$b = \sqrt{a^2 + c^2 - 2ac \, \cos B}$$

$$c = \sqrt{a^2 + b^2 - 2ab \, \cos C}$$

Solve the following oblique triangles:

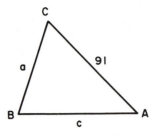

1. Given: b = 91, A = 46 degrees 19 minutes, B = 71 degrees 39
   minutes. Find a, c, and C.   _____

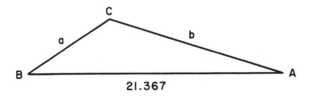

2. Given: c = 21.367, C = 130 degrees 42 minutes 18 seconds, A = 17
   degrees 17 minutes 41 seconds. Find a, b, and B.   _____

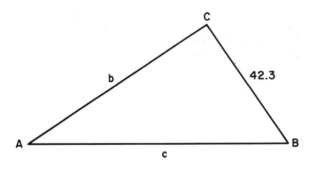

3. Given: a = 42.3, A = 67 degrees 18 minutes 14 seconds, B = 48
   degrees 13 minutes 8 seconds. Find b, c, and C.   _____

4. Given: b = 2674, A = 32 degrees 14 minutes, C = 92 degrees 19
   minutes. Find a, c, and B.   _____

5. Given: a = 42.3, A = 67 degrees 18 minutes 14 seconds, B = 48
   degrees 13 minutes 8 seconds. Find b, c, and C.   _____

Unit 70 PRACTICAL PROBLEMS

BASIC PRINCIPLES OF TRIGONOMETRY

- Review unit 79 in *Basic Mathematics Simplified* for the Laws of Sines and Cosines.
- Apply the Laws of Sines and Cosines to the work of the machinist by solving the Review Problems which follow.

REVIEW PROBLEMS

Determine the number of solutions in each of the following triangles and find the unknown parts:

1. Given: a = 16.3   c = 21   A = 37 degrees 15 minutes   _____

2. Given: b = 142   c = 209   C = 57 degrees 15 minutes   _____

3. Given: a = 2.37   b = 3.26   B = 16 degrees 17 minutes   _____

4. Given: b = 1.792 a = 1.727   A = 74 degrees 33 minutes   _____

5. The distance between two points A and B is 6.864 inches. At a   _____
   point C, 7.822 inches from A, the angle ACB is found to be 31 degrees
   12 minutes. What is the distance from C to B?

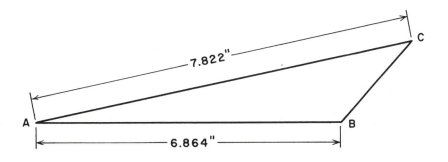

6. A draftsman is required to give a dimension between two points B   _____
   and C on a drawing. The distance from a third point A, to B and C
   respectively, is 4.236 inches and 2.769 inches. The angle C equals 48
   degrees 27 minutes. Draw a sketch and find the required dimensions.

7. At a point 5762 feet from the nearer of two milestones on a level   _____
   plane, an observer finds the angle between them to be 23 degrees 7
   minutes 15 seconds. What is the distance to the other milestone?

8. The boom of a ship derrick is inclined at an angle of 27 degrees with   _____
   the horizontal. At a point on the boom 17 feet from its base, a tie
   rod 15 1/2 feet long extends to the mast. Find the distance from the
   foot of the boom to each of two points at which the brace can be
   fastened to the mast.

Unit 71 OBLIQUE TRIANGLES

BASIC PRINCIPLES OF TRIGONOMETRY

- Review unit 79 in *Basic Mathematics Simplified* for the principles of oblique triangles.
- Apply the principles of oblique triangles to the work of the machinist by solving the Review Problems which follow

REVIEW PROBLEMS

Solve the following triangles:

1. a = 273.4   b = 627   C = 21 degrees 17 minutes   _____

2. c = 276   b = 418   A = 126 degrees 19 minutes   _____

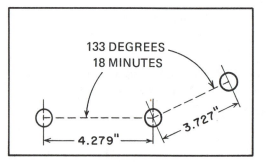

3. A toolmaker is required to lay out three holes in a plate, as shown on   _____
    the diagram. What is the distance between the first and third holes?

4. Find the length of the belt, as illustrated.   _____

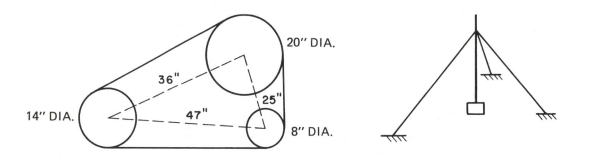

5. The pole, as shown, is braced by 3 guy wires attached 53 feet above   _____
    the base and 120 degrees around the pole. Each guy wire makes an
    angle of 38 degrees with the pole. If the pole is situated on a 26
    degree slope with one guy wire running directly down the slope, find
    the length of each of the three wires.

SECTION 13 — BELT DRIVES AND GEAR TRAINS

Unit 72 PULLEY SPEEDS

REVIEW OF BASIC PRINCIPLES

- Review units 51-53 in *Basic Mathematics Simplified* for the principle of ratio and proportion.

- Apply the principles of ratio and proportion and its relation to belt drives and gear train to the work of the machinist by solving the Review Problems which follow.

REVIEW PROBLEMS

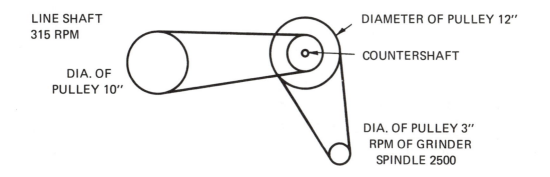

LINE SHAFT 315 RPM

DIA. OF PULLEY 10"

DIAMETER OF PULLEY 12"

COUNTERSHAFT

DIA. OF PULLEY 3"
RPM OF GRINDER SPINDLE 2500

In the diagram of the drive of a grinder, find the following:

1. The speed of the countershaft. _____

2. The speed in feet per minute of the belt driving the countershaft. _____

3. The speed of the belt driving the grinder pulley. _____

4. The size of the pulley that is required on the line shaft to drive the grinder 2500 revolutions per minute direct without a countershaft. _____

5. A driven pulley has a 10-inch and a 12-inch step. The driving cone running at 200 revolutions per minute has a 6 1/8-inch step. What driven cone-pulley speeds result? _____

6. A motor with a 12-inch pulley running at 1140 revolutions per minute is to drive a line shaft at 225 revolutions per minute. Find the necessary pulley diameter. _____

7. A 6-inch pulley running 1740 revolutions per minute drives an 18-inch pulley at 580 revolutions per minute. What is the belt speed in feet per minute? _____

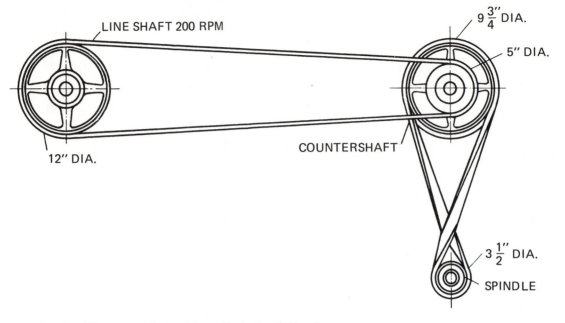

LINE SHAFT 200 RPM

$9\frac{3}{4}''$ DIA.

5″ DIA.

12″ DIA.

COUNTERSHAFT

$3\frac{1}{2}''$ DIA.

SPINDLE

In the illustrated belt drive, find the following:

8. The rpm of the countershaft. _____

9. The rpm of the spindle. _____

10. The speed of the belt driving the countershaft. _____

11. The speed of the belt driving the spindle. _____

12. A 36-inch driving pulley, mounted on a line shaft turning at 200 _____
    revolutions per minute is belted to a 14-inch countershaft pulley. A
    belt from a 24-inch countershaft pulley turns a 7-inch pulley on a
    grinding wheel stand. Find the revolutions per minute of the
    grinding wheel.

13. The accompanying diagram represents the drive of a dynamo under a _____
    railroad passenger car. A 40-inch car wheel, A, is on the same axle as
    a 16-inch pulley, B. The 10-inch pulley, C, drives the dynamo. Find
    the revolutions per minute of the dynamo when the car travels at
    40 miles per hour.

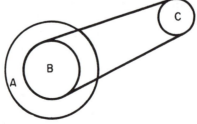

14. A driving shaft turns at 145 revolutions per minute. A pulley diam- _____
    eter must be found to drive an 11-inch pulley at 800 revolutions per
    minute through a jack-shaft having a 10-inch driven and a 20-inch
    driving pulley.

Unit 73 GEAR SPEED AND DIRECTION

BASIC PRINCIPLES OF GEAR SPEED AND DIRECTION

- Review units 51-53 in *Basic Mathematics Simplified* for the principles of ratio and proportion as it applies to gear speed and direction.

- Apply the principles of gear speed and direction to the work of the machinist by solving the Review Problems which follow.

REVIEW PROBLEMS

1. Find the speed of the driven shaft when the driving shaft turns at 400 revolutions per minute and the following four gears are in a train, as illustrated.

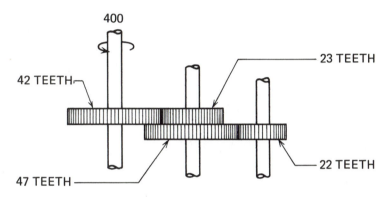

2. Give the speed and direction of each of the four gears in the diagram, if the driver turns 75 revolutions per minute, right-handed.

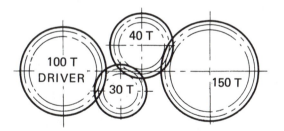

3. Find the speed and direction of an 80-tooth driver to drive, through three idlers, a gear of 75 teeth turning 160 revolutions per minute, left-handed.

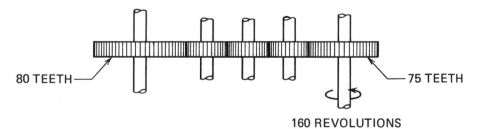

160 REVOLUTIONS

4. Give speed and direction of each gear shown in the illustrated train. _____

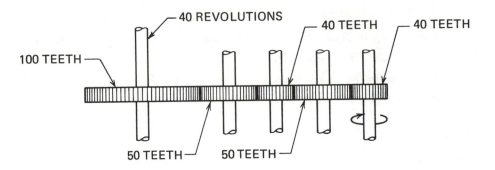

Solve the following problems related to this diagram:

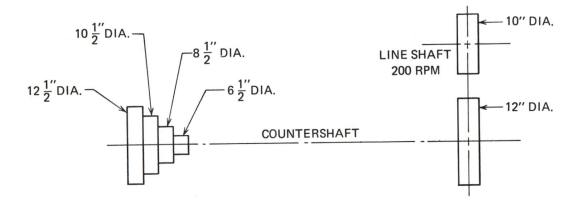

5. Find the revolutions per minute of the countershaft. _____

6. Find the revolutions per minute of the spindle for each step of the cones with the back gears out. _____

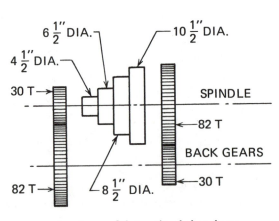

7. Find the revolutions per minute of the spindle for each step of the cones with the back gears in. _____

8. A 1200-revolutions per minute motor having a 24-tooth pinion is to drive a machine at 225 revolutions per minute. How many teeth must the driven gear have? _____

Unit 74 CHANGE GEAR DRIVES

BASIC PRINCIPLES OF CHANGE GEAR DRIVES

- Review units 51-53 in *Basic Mathematics Simplified* for the principles of change gear drives.

- Apply the principles of change gear drives to the work of the machinist by solving the Review Problems which follow.

REVIEW PROBLEMS

Note: Speeds are controlled by sliding clutches. In the sketch below all clutches are shown in neutral position.

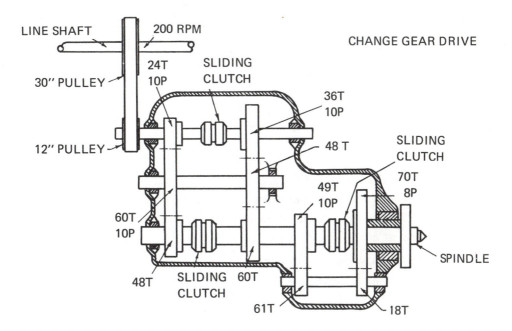

1. This geared head arrangement provides eight speeds. Find the eight speeds and arrange the answers in a table similar to the one which follows.

RANGE OF SPINDLE REVOLUTIONS PER MINUTE							
Slowest	Second	Third	Fourth	Fifth	Sixth	Seventh	Highest

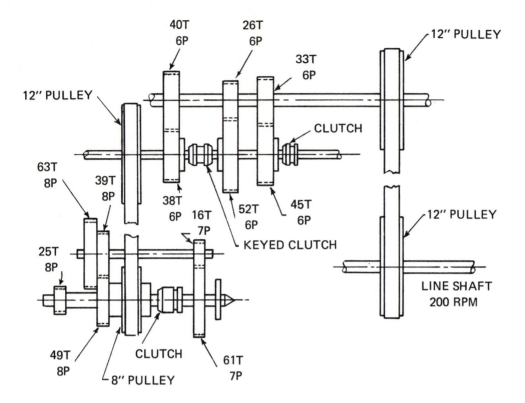

Note: Through the arrangement of gears on the countershaft shown in the sketch, three direct spindle speeds are possible. There are two sets of back gears, each set providing an additional three speeds, making nine speeds in all.

2. Find the nine spindle speeds and arrange the answers in a chart similar to the one which follows.

RANGE OF SPINDLE REVOLUTIONS PER MINUTE								
Slowest	Second	Third	Fourth	Fifth	Sixth	Seventh	Eighth	Highest

3. If a 2 1/2-inch piece of stock is turned in the lathe shown with a cutting tool designed for 115 feet per minute cutting speed, how many revolutions per minute does the spindle turn and what is the nearest speed?

_____

4. A 9 3/4-inch piece of steel is turned on the same lathe, on the next to lowest speed. What is the cutting speed of the tool?

_____

Unit 75 POWER OF BELTING

BASIC PRINCIPLES APPLIED TO POWER OF BELTING

- Review units 63 and 66 in *Basic Mathematics Simplified.*

- Apply the principles of power of belting to the work of the machinist by solving the Review Problems which follow.

REVIEW PROBLEMS

Note: A belt connecting two pulleys has a tension in it due to the weight of the belt and the initial tension under which the belt was stretched over the pulleys. When the pulleys are at rest the tension is the same in all parts of the belt. $T_1 = T_2$

If the driving pulley is turned, the tension in the tight, or pulling, side of the belt increases. When the tension becomes great enough to overcome the force which is retarding the driven pulley, the driven pulley will turn. This difference $T_1 - T_2$, is called the effective pull, and it will be seen that the greater the difference the more power will be transmitted.

It has been found that, to avoid slipping of the belt on the pulley, T_1 should not be more than 2 1/3 times T_2. The ratio of tight to slack sides of the belt may be written $T_1/T_2 = 7/3$.

The tension in the tight side, T, should not be over 75 pounds per inch width of belt for single belts, nor over 140 pounds per inch width for double ply belts.

1. Find the effective pull for a 3-inch double belt. T is 140 pounds per inch width.   _____

2. Find the tension in the slack side of a 4-inch single belt. T_1 is 75 pounds per inch width.   _____

$$\text{Horsepower} = \frac{(T_1 - T_2) \times \text{width in inches} \times \text{feet per minute}}{33,000}$$

3. Find the width of the single belt necessary to transmit 20 horsepower at 3200 feet per minute. T_1 equals 70 pounds per inch.   _____

4. What horsepower can be transmitted by a 4-inch single belt running from a 48-inch pulley at 100 revolutions per minute?   _____

5. What horsepower could be transmitted if a double belt were used in the preceding problem?   _____

6. A 2-inch belt driving a 6-inch diameter pulley at 600 revolutions per minute is to transmit 3 1/2 horsepower. T_1 will equal 2 1/3 T_2. With what tension per inch of width must the belt be placed on the pulleys? Is the belt single or double?   _____   _____

7. A 12-inch pulley turning at 145 revolutions per minute is driven by a 4-inch single belt. What horsepower is being transmitted by the belt, if $T_1 - T_2$ is 43 pounds per inch of belt width? _____

8. Determine the horsepower for the preceding problem by the millwright's rule (A single belt traveling 600 feet per minute will transmit one horsepower for every inch of width.) _____

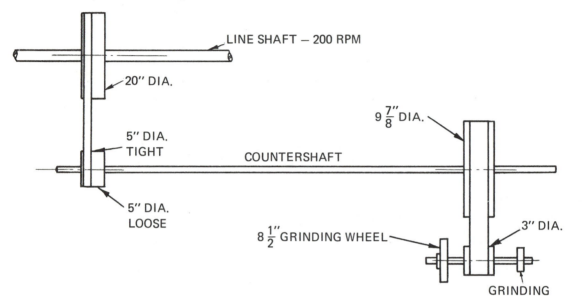

In the preceding sketch, find the following:

9. The rpm of the countershaft. _____

10. The rpm of the spindle. _____

11. The surface speed of the 8 1/2-inch grinding wheel. _____

12. The diameter of the small grinding wheel if its surface speed is 3913 feet per minute. _____

13. What horsepower can be transmitted by a 5 1/2-inch single belt running from a 48-inch pulley at 140 revolutions per minute? _____

14. What horsepower could be transmitted if a double belt were used in the preceding problem? _____

15. Determine the width of a single belt necessary to transmit 20 horsepower at 3200 feet per minute. _____

16. How wide a double belt would be used in the preceding problem? _____

17. What is the speed in feet per minute of a 10-inch single belt that transmits 15 horsepower? _____

Unit 76 PRACTICAL PROBLEMS

BASIC PRINCIPLES APPLIED TO GEAR COMPUTATIONS

- Review units 63 and 66 in *Basic Mathematics Simplified.*
- Apply the principles of gear formulas to the work of the machinist by solving the Review Problems which follow.

REVIEW PROBLEMS

References: *Machinery's Handbook, Brown and Sharpe Treatise on Gearing.*

N = No. of teeth	D"= Working Depth	
P = Diametral Pitch	S = Addendum	
P' = Circular Pitch	T = Thickness of Tooth	
D = Outside Diameter	D" + F = Whole Depth	
D'= Pitch Diameter	F = Clearance	

1. A gear has an 8 diametral pitch and 32 teeth. Find the following:

Pitch Diameter	_____	Tooth Space	_____
Addendum	_____	Clearance	_____
Outside Diameter	_____	Dedendum	_____
Circular Pitch	_____	Fillet Radius	_____
Tooth Width	_____		

2. A gear has a circular pitch of 1 1/2 inches and 64 teeth.

Pitch Diameter	_____	Tooth Space	_____
Addendum	_____	Clearance	_____
Outside Diameter	_____	Dedendum	_____
Diametral Pitch	_____	Fillet Radius	_____
Tooth Width	_____		

3. The outside diameter of a gear measures 5.25 inches. It has 40 teeth. Find the following:

Pitch Diameter	_____	Tooth Space	_____
Addendum	_____	Clearance	_____
Diametral Pitch	_____	Dedendum	_____
Tooth Width	_____	Fillet Radius	_____

4. A gear has 50 teeth. The tooth width is 1/2 inch. Find the following:

   Pitch Diameter   _____   Diametral Pitch   _____

   Addendum   _____   Clearance   _____

   Outside Diameter   _____   Dedendum   _____

   Circular Pitch   _____   Fillet Radius   _____

   Tooth Space   _____

5. Find the remaining dimensions of a spur gear which has 30 teeth and a .7854-inch circular pitch.

6. A spur gear has a 12-inch pitch diameter and 72 teeth. Find the circular pitch.

7. A stripped spur gear has 32 teeth and is 8 diametral pitch. Find the pitch diameter and the outside diameter.

8. Find the thickness of tooth, working depth, and addendum of a spur gear of 7 diametral pitch.

9. A spur gear has 36 teeth and addendum .250 inch. What is the outside diameter?

10. A 4-pitch spur gear has 24 teeth. Find the remaining dimensions necessary to give full information for a drawing.

11. A gear of 12 pitch has 60 teeth. Find the clearance, addendum, outside diameter, and the working depth.

12. What is the thickness of tooth on a 12-pitch gear?

13. Find the total depth of a tooth on a 10-pitch gear?

14. Two 8-pitch gears, to accomplish a three to one reduction have respectively, 17 and 51 teeth. How far apart are their centers?

15. Two spur gears of 6 pitch have a center distance of 14.666 inches and a ratio of 4 to 7. How many teeth are there in each gear?

16. What is the working depth of tooth on a 13-pitch gear?

17. Find the outside diameter of a gear blank for 96 teeth, 14 pitch.

18. What is the outside diameter of a gear blank for a gear of 60 teeth and circular pitch of .2618 inch?

19. A gear blank is to be made for a gear of 71 teeth at 11 pitch. What is the outside diameter of the blank?

20. Determine the outside diameter of a gear of 128 teeth, 8 pitch.

21. What is the gear blank diameter for a 100-tooth gear with circular pitch of .1963 inch?

22. A broken gear has 21 teeth and measures approximately 6 11/16 inches for the outside diameter. Find the pitch and pitch diameter.

23. In repairing a machine, it is necessary to replace two broken gears, one 4.2222 inches in diameter with 36 teeth and the other 10.400 inches in diameter with 50 teeth. What pitch cutters are used to cut the teeth of these gears?

24. Two gears in mesh, having a 4 to 9 ratio, provide feed for a special machine. The larger has 45 teeth and the center distance is 3.25 inches. What is the diametral pitch of these gears and the number of teeth in the smaller one?

25. Two gears, A and B, have a ratio of 3 to 7, with intermediate gear C to reverse the direction of rotation. C is an 8 pitch gear of 17 teeth and the center distance A to B is 9 inches. Find the pitch diameter and number of teeth in A and B.

26. A gear is 6 diametral pitch with 26 teeth. Find the addendum and diameter of gear blank.

27. A gear of 23 teeth has an outside diameter of 3.125 inches. Find the diametral pitch.

28. Find the chordal thickness of tooth in the preceding problem.

29. Determine the corrected addendum to be used in measuring the tooth in problem 27.

30. Find the center distance of two 10 pitch gears running together, if the larger has 92 teeth and the smaller, 45 teeth.

31. What size blank is needed for a 7 pitch gear of 31 teeth?

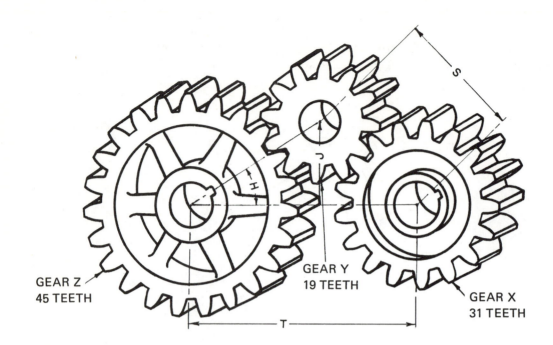

GEAR Z
45 TEETH

GEAR Y
19 TEETH

GEAR X
31 TEETH

Note: Distance "T" equals 5.5 inches.   Distance "S" equals 3.125 inches.   Refer to the sketch in solving the following problems.

32. Find the chordal thickness in gear Z.   _____

33. Find the chordal thickness in gear Y.   _____

34. Find the center distance in gears Y and Z.   _____

35. Find the outside diameter of gear X.   _____

36. Find the pitch diameter of gear Y.   _____

37. Find the diametral pitch of each of the gears.   _____

38. What is the corrected addendum of gear X?   _____

39. What is the outside diameter of gear Y?   _____

40. What is the outside diameter of gear Z?   _____

41. Find the value of angle H.   _____

42. Find the distance J.   _____

Unit 77 CUTTING SPEEDS

BASIC PRINCIPLES APPLIED TO CUTTING SPEEDS

- • Review units 63 and 66 in *Basic Mathematics Simplified.*

- • Apply the use of formulas to the work of the machinist by solving the Review Problems which follow.

REVIEW PROBLEMS

1. A piece of cast iron 7/8 inch in diameter is turned in a lathe at 168 revolutions per minute. Find the cutting speed.   _____

2. How many revolutions per minute are required to turn a gear blank, 4.5 inches in diameter, at a cutting speed of 42 feet per minute?   _____

3. A piece of tool steel 3/4 inch in diameter is turned in a lathe. How many revolutions per minute are necessary to give a cutting speed of 30 feet per minute?   _____

4. In turning a cast iron pulley, 14 inches in diameter, what revolutions per minute are necessary with a cutting speed of 46 feet per minute?   _____

5. Determine the cutting speed required to turn a brass rod 1 1/4 inches in diameter at 252 revolutions per minute.   _____

6. A steel cylinder 1 inch in diameter has a flange 3 inches in diameter at one end. What are the necessary revolutions per minute to obtain a cutting speed of 60 feet per minute?   _____

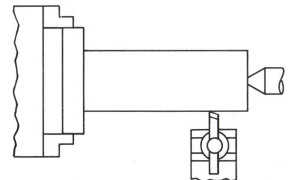

7. It is desired to turn a 3/8-inch diameter screw at 70 feet per minute. A thread is to be chased at 20 feet per minute. Find the respective speeds in revolutions per minute.   _____

8. A cut meter shows the surface speed to be 65 feet per minute. The stock is turning at 65 revolutions per minute. What is the diameter of the stock?   _____

Unit 78 TAPERS

BASIC PRINCIPLES APPLIED TO TAPERS

- Review units 63 and 66 in *Basic Mathematics Simplified.*

- Apply the use of formulas to the work of the machinist by solving the Review Problems which follow.

REVIEW PROBLEMS

1. A taper 6 5/8 inches long measures 2.375 inches at one end and 1.428 inches at the other. What is the taper per foot?   _____

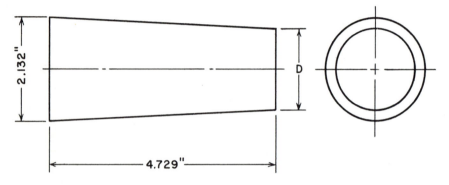

2. The piece shown in the drawing has a taper of 1.105 inches per foot. Find dimension D.   _____

3. If a piece of work has the dimensions shown in the diagram, what is the diameter at the large end?   _____

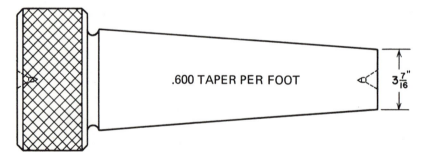

.600 TAPER PER FOOT

4. Find the length of a taper which is .486 inch larger at one end than at the other, if it tapers at the rate of .750 inch per foot.   _____

5. A piece of work 3 1/4 inches in diameter at the large end and 2 5/16 inches at the small end tapers at the rate of 1 1/16 inches to the foot. How long is it?   _____

6. If a piece of work tapers at the rate of 5/8 inch to the foot, how much does it taper in 19 3/4 inches?   _____

7. A piece of work 28 3/8 inches long is 1.763 inches larger at one end than it is at the other. What is the rate of taper per foot?   _____

160

8. The taper ring gage shown in the sketch has a taper of 5/8 inch per foot. A scratch on the plug gage is located such that when the plug is half inserted into the ring gage, the scratch will be 1/16 inch above the end of the ring. How much larger is the plug gage at the scratch than the large end of the ring gage? (Carry the answer to four places.)

_____

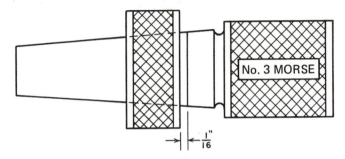

9. A machinist is boring a Brown and Sharpe taper hole on a lathe. The rate of taper is 1/2 inch per foot. He uses the compound rest which he has set on the correct size, and has taken the next to the final cut. Upon trying the plug gage in the hole, he finds that it fits to within 3/4 inch of the correct depth. How much should he adjust the cross feed for the final cut?

_____

10. Look up the directions for determining the dimensions of Jarno tapers in *Machinery's Handbook,* and give the following data for a number 9 Jarno taper: diameter at large end, length, and taper per foot.

_____
_____
_____

11. A piece of work is 9 3/4 inches long. Throughout 2/3 of its length, the piece is straight, and the remaining 1/3 tapers at the rate of .600 inch per foot. If the diameter at the large end is 1.785 inches, what is the diameter at the small end?

_____

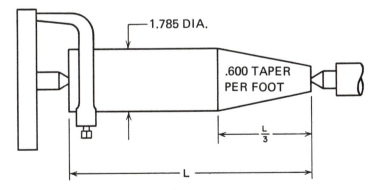

Note: The tailstock may be offset either toward the tool or away from it. If the offset is toward the tool, the work will increase in diameter toward the head of the lathe.

12. A piece of work 12 inches long is to taper 7/16 inch in its length. How much should the tailstock be offset to turn the taper?

13. What is the correct amount to offset a lathe tailstock to turn a Morse taper (5/8 inch per foot) 7 1/4 inches in length?

14. A number 9 Standard taper pin is .591 inches in diameter at its large end and is 5 1/4 inches long. If the rate of taper is 1/4 inch per foot, what is the diameter at the small end. How much should the tailstock be set over to turn the taper?

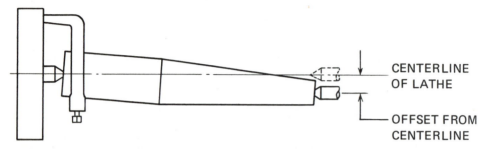

CENTERLINE
OF LATHE

OFFSET FROM
CENTERLINE

Note: In making calculations for offsetting the tailstock to turn a taper that extends but part of the length of the piece, the machinist must bear in mind the following: the tailstock must be offset just as much as though the taper were to continue at the same rate throughout the entire length. A study of the following sketch may help to make this clear.

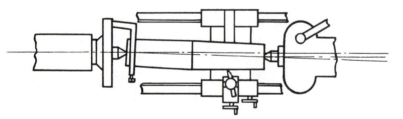

15. A machinist is required to turn a taper, as shown on the diagram. Find the diameter at the small end and the amount of necessary tailstock setover.

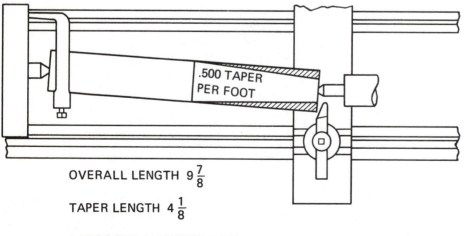

.500 TAPER
PER FOOT

OVERALL LENGTH 9 $\frac{7}{8}$

TAPER LENGTH 4 $\frac{1}{8}$

LARGE END DIAMETER 1.346

16. A piece of work is to be partially tapered, as illustrated. The taper extends one-third of the length of the workpiece. Find the difference in the diameters at the large and small ends, and the amount to offset the tailstock.

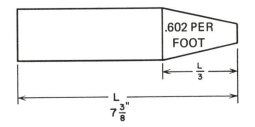

17. The included angle of a taper is 4 degrees 13 minutes, the length of the taper is 9 1/4 inches, and the diameter is 1.875 inches at the small end. What is the diameter of the large end?

18. In the drawing, the pulley is to have a crown of 7/8 of an inch to the foot. The mandrel is 9 inches in length. How much should the tailstock of the lathe be set over, and what is the angle of the crown?

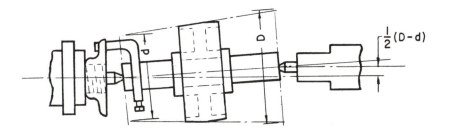

19. Determine the amount of taper in a workpiece 9 inches long with a 3/4 inch per foot taper.

20. Determine the amount of taper and the diameter of the large end for a Brown and Sharpe number 11 taper. The small end is 1.25 inches, as shown, and the length is 6 3/4 inches.

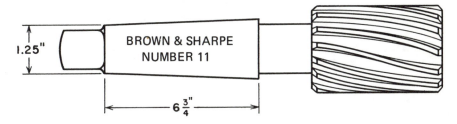

21. A piece 11 1/2 inches long is turned with a taper of .602 inch per foot. The taper has a large diameter of 7 1/16 inches and a length equal to 3/4 of the total length of the piece. What is the small diameter?

22. The large diameter of the shank of a tapered arbor is 2 inches at a   _____
    point 6 inches from the end. The small end measures 1 7/16 inches.
    What is the taper per foot?

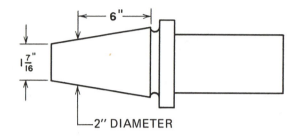

23. A workpiece is .725 inch at one end; at the other end it measures   _____
    .580 inch.   If the taper is 1/4 inch per foot, what is the length
    of the piece?

24. Determine the setover for a Brown and Sharpe taper 5 inches long.   _____

25. If a Brown and Sharpe taper 5 inches long is to be turned on the end   _____
    of a straight shaft 10 inches long, what setover is required?

26. Determine the tailstock offset to turn a number 3 Brown and Sharpe   _____
    taper on a milling machine arbor 14 inches long.

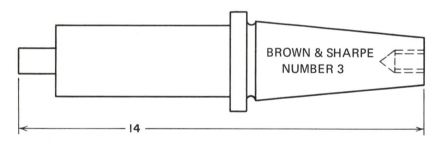

27. Determine the tailstock setover for grinding a taper reamer 1.1875   _____
    inches diameter on the small end, 1.375 inches on the large end, and
    6 inches long, with a 4 1/2-inch shank.

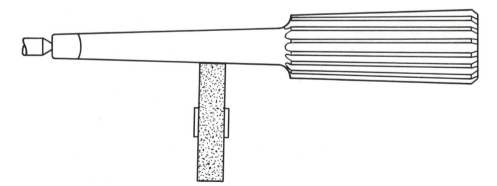

Unit 79 SCREW THREADS

BASIC PRINCIPLES APPLIED TO SCREW THREADS

- Review units 63 and 66 in *Basic Mathematics Simplified.*
- Apply the principles of screw threads to the work of the machinist by solving the Review Problems which follow.

REVIEW PROBLEMS

Note: In the following problems assume the lathe to have these gears: 25, 30, 35, 40, 50, 60, 65, 70, 75, 80, 85, 90, 95, 100, 110, and 120.

1. Select the correct gearing for 13 threads per inch.   The stud rotates at the same speed as the spindle and the lead screw has 6 threads.   _____

2. A lathe on which the stud turns at the same rate as the spindle has a 30-tooth gear on the stud and a 110-tooth gear on the screw. How many turns does the spindle make when the screw turns once?   _____

3. Select gears to cut 10 threads if the lead screw has 4 threads per inch.   _____

4. With a lathe constant of 6, select gears to cut 9 1/2 threads per inch.   _____

5. If the lead screw has 6 threads per inch and the spindle turns 1 1/2 turns for one of the stud, what is the lathe constant?   _____

6. In order to obtain two turns of a spindle for one of the screws when a 60-tooth gear is used on the screw, what gear must be placed on the stud?   The ratio of the spindle to the stud is 1 to 1.   _____

   Note: In the following problems assume the lathe to have these gears: 25, 30, 35, 40, 45, 50, 55, 60, 65, 70, 75, 80, 85, 90, 100, 110, 120.

7. Determine the gears to cut 20 threads per inch with a 4-threads-per-inch lead screw.   A 2 to 1 compound will be used.   _____

8. Determine the gears necessary, if a 3 to 1 compound were used in problem 7.   _____

Unit 80 DRILLING AND TURNING

BASIC PRINCIPLES APPLIED TO DRILLING

- • Review units 63 and 66 in *Basic Mathematics Simplified.*

- • Apply basic principles of drilling to the work of the machinist by solving the Review Problems which follow.

REVIEW PROBLEMS

1. At what speed should a 3/4-inch high speed drill be run to drill a hole through a block of machine steel 1 3/4 inches thick?   _____

2. Estimate the time necessary for drilling a 3/8-inch diameter hole through a piece of 1/2-inch cold rolled steel. A high speed steel drill is used at 70 feet per minute with a .005-inch feed.   _____

3. With a .003-inch feed, how long does it take to drill a 3/16-inch hole through a 3/4-inch piece of cold rolled steel with a high speed drill?   _____

4. Estimate the time required to take one roughing cut on a mild steel machine spindle 1 1/4 inch in diameter and 17 inches long. Allow 50 seconds for changing the lathe dog.   _____

5. How fast should a cast iron pulley 10 inches in diameter turn, using a high speed tool? How long will it take to make one cut across the face of the pulley, as shown, with a feed of .018 inches?   _____
   _____

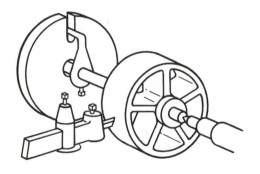

6. A machine steel forging is finished to the dimensions illustrated, using high speed tools at 75 revolutions per minute. Estimate the turning time, if 1/8 inch of stock has been left for finishing.   _____

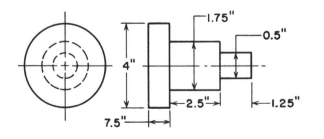

Unit 81 PRACTICAL PROBLEMS

REVIEW OF BASIC PRINCIPLES

- Review units 63 and 66 in *Basic Mathematics Simplified.*
- Apply the principles of cutting speed conversion to the work of the machinist by solving the Review Problems which follow.

REVIEW PROBLEMS

1. How many revolutions per minute are necessary to turn a piece of machine steel 1 3/4 inches in diameter, at a speed of 35 feet per minute? _____

2. What number of revolutions per minute are necessary for a cutting speed of 40 feet per minute when turning a cold rolled steel shaft 2 5/8 inches in diameter? _____

3. Estimate the time required to turn a machine steel reamer shank, in two cuts, from 1 3/4-inch diameter to 1 5/8-inch diameter. The piece is 10 inches long and a feed of .015 inch is used at a cutting speed of 65 feet per minute.

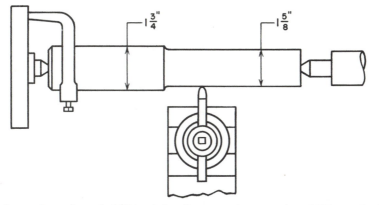

4. A piece of cast iron 1 1/8 inch in diameter is turned at 150 revolutions per minute. What is the cutting speed? Is this the correct speed for a carbon steel cutting tool? What should it be for a high speed tool? _____ _____ _____

5. What speed is used to turn a steel gear blank having a diameter of 5.25 inches, when cutting at 70 feet per minute? _____

6. The cast iron cylinder, shown in the drawing, is to be turned at 50 feet per minute. What should be the revolutions per minute for the two steps? For facing? _____ _____

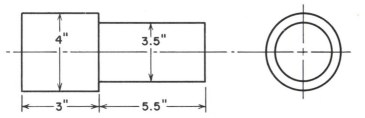

Unit 82 CUTTER SPEEDS

BASIC PRINCIPLES APPLIED TO CUTTER SPEEDS

- Review units 63 and 66 in *Basic Mathematics Simplified*.
- Apply the principles of cutter speeds to the work of the machinist by solving the Review Problems which follow.

REVIEW PROBLEMS

1. A milling cutter 2 inches in diameter is running at 80 revolutions per minute. Find the cutting speed. _____

2. A milling cutter 3 3/4 inches in diameter is running at 70 revolutions per minute. Find the cutting speed. _____

3. A milling cutter turning at 25 revolutions per minute is cutting at a speed of 36 feet per minute.   Find the diameter of the cutter. _____

4. A milling cutter 4 inches in diameter is cutting at a speed of 76.69 feet per minute.   How many revolutions per minute is it turning? _____

5. How much time is required to mill a 16-inch long cut, if the feed is .008 inch and the speed, 125 revolutions per minute? _____

6. How long does it take to mill a groove 8 inches long, with a feed of 7/8 inch per minute? _____

7. Estimate the time required to mill the tops of 24 pieces which are 12 inches long.   The feed is 1 1/2 inches per minute and 1 minute is allowed between cuts. _____

8. The cutting speed is 60 feet per minute; the diameter of the cutter, 3.8 inches.   Find the time required to mill 18 inches with a .033-inch feed. _____

9. A 24-inch cut is completed in 8 minutes. What is the average feed per tooth of an 18-tooth cutter turning 60 revolutions per minute? _____

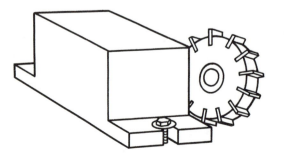

Unit 83 INDEXING

BASIC PRINCIPLES OF INDEXING

- Review units 63 and 66 in *Basic Mathematics Simplified*.
- Apply principles of indexing to the work of the machinist by solving the Review Problems which follow.

REVIEW PROBLEMS

PLATE # 1	PLATE # 2	PLATE # 3
15 holes	21 holes	37 holes
16 holes	23 holes	39 holes
17 holes	27 holes	41 holes
18 holes	29 holes	43 holes
19 holes	31 holes	47 holes
20 holes	33 holes	49 holes

1. What circles on the preceding plates may be used to obtain the following: (Give all the possible answers, including the number of holes the pin is moved and the number of holes in the circle.)

    a. 1/7 turn of the crank _____   f. 1/43 turn of the crank _____

    b. 1/4 turn of the crank _____   g. 1/11 turn of the crank _____

    c. 1/8 turn of the crank _____   h. 1/15 turn of the crank _____

    d. 1/9 turn of the crank _____   i. 1/17 turn of the crank _____

    e. 1/19 turn of the crank _____   j. 1/5 turn of the crank _____

    Note: To find the indexing (the turns of the crank and the circle to use) for any required number of divisions of the rim of a piece of work (such as teeth in a gear) proceed as in the following examples:

    Note: The standard equipment of an indexing head does not provide means for every number of divisions by simple or plain indexing. Methods known as compound and differential indexing are required for some divisions.

    Example: Find the indexing for 24 divisions (gear teeth). Since 40 turns of the crank turn the gear blank once, for 24 divisions, as required, the crank would be turned 40 ÷ 24 = 1 2/3 turns to each division. The 2/3 turn could be made in any of the following circles: 15, 18, 33, 39. Taking the 15-hole circle the correct indexing would be one turn and ten holes.

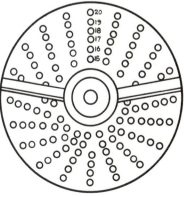

Note: The following index plates which will take all numbers up to 58, even numbers up to 100 and others as high as 360, are to be used in the solution of the problems following:

First plate,   34, 39, 46, 51, 58   Third plate,   37, 42, 48, 54, 62

Second plate,   36, 41, 47, 53, 60   Fourth plate,   38, 43, 49, 56, 66

2. Calculate the index for 17 divisions. _____

3. Calculate the index for 120 divisions. _____

4. Index for 112 divisions. _____

5. Calculate the number of turns and holes to mill a hexagon, using a dividing head. _____
_____

6. Index for 29 divisions with a 40 to 1 head. _____

For the following problems use the list of index plates at the top of page 169.

7. Fill in a table similar to the following:

DIVISIONS REQUIRED	HOLES IN INDEX CIRCLE	NUMBER OF TURNS OF CRANK
3		
5		
6		
7		
11		
16		
19		
20		
21		
	39	1 26/39
	33	1 22/33
	18	1 12/18
36		
45		
49		
54		
	29	10/29
	39	20/39
	47	20/47
220		
276		

Unit 84 PRACTICAL PROBLEMS

BASIC PRINCIPLES APPLIED TO MILLING MACHINE WORK

- Review units 63 and 66 in *Basic Mathematics Simplified.*
- Apply basic principles of milling to the work of the machinist by solving the Review Problems which follow.

REVIEW PROBLEMS

1. At how many revolutions per minute should a 4 1/4-inch shell end mill (see illustration) be run to mill the edge of a machine steel plate 1 inch wide? _____

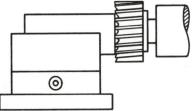

2. The cast iron angle plate, as illustrated, is to be milled with a 6-inch diameter inserted-tooth face mill. If the teeth are high speed steel, what are the revolutions per minute, the feed, and time required for a rough and finish cut? _____
_____
_____

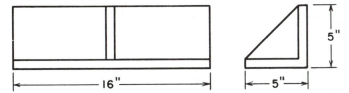

3. At how many revolutions per minute should a 5 1/2-inch diameter cutter be run to cut the slot in the cast iron slide, as illustrated? Estimate the time, using a .038-inch feed. _____

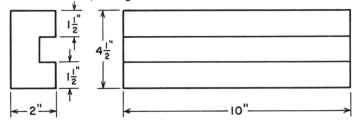

4. Find the revolutions per minute of a high speed steel Tee-slot cutter to cut the slot in a cast iron adjusting block, shown in the accompanying sketch. _____

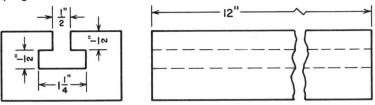

Unit 85 PLANER SPEEDS

BASIC PRINCIPLES APPLIED TO PLANER SPEEDS

- Review units 51-53 in *Basic Mathematics Simplified.*

- Apply the principles of ratio and proportions, special formulas, and handbook data in planer and shaper work to the work of the machinist by solving the Review Problems which follow.

REVIEW PROBLEMS

1. Find the effective cutting speed in feet per minute, when a planer has a forward speed of 20 feet per minute and a return 3 times as fast. _____

2. What is the effective cutting speed of a planer which has a forward speed of 30 feet per minute and a return speed of 45 feet per minute? _____

3. A planer has a forward speed of 50 feet per minute and a reverse speed of 70 feet per minute. Find the number of strokes per minute, when a stroke 5 feet long is used. _____

4. Find the effective cutting speed of a planer making 14 strokes per minute. The length of the stroke is 3 1/2 feet, and the return ratio is 3 to 1. _____

5. Find the time required to take one complete cut over the top surface of a casting measuring 4 feet by 10 feet, using a feed of 1/4 inch on a planer with a forward speed of 20 feet per minute and a reverse of 40 feet per minute. _____

6. A planer with a 7 foot by 3 foot bed has a cutting stroke of 40 feet per minute and a return of 60 feet per minute. Estimate the time needed to finish two surface plates each 2 feet by 3 feet. The feed for roughing may be 1/16 inch and for finishing 3/16 inch. _____

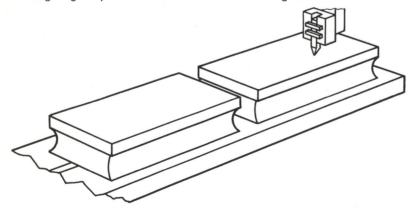

Unit 86 NET CUTTING SPEEDS

BASIC PRINCIPLES APPLIED TO CUTTING SPEEDS

- Review units 51-53 and 66 in *Basic Mathematics Simplified.*
- Apply the principles of ratio and proportion, special formulas, and handbook data in shaper work to the work of the machinist by solving the Review Problems which follow.

REVIEW PROBLEMS

Note: In the following problems, the term "net cutting speed" means the speed of the tool during the cutting stroke and the term "effective or average cutting speed" means the rate at which the work is being accomplished, including the time of both cutting and return strokes.

1. Find the net cutting speed of a shaper running 24 strokes per minute with a forward stroke of 1 foot and a return of 2 to 1.   _____

2. What is the effective cutting speed in the preceding problem?   _____

3. Find the net cutting speed of a shaper making 48 strokes per minute, when the length of stroke is 8 inches.   _____

4. A shaper makes 36 strokes per minute and has a 2 to 1 reverse. What is the net cutting speed on a 16-inch stroke?   _____

5. On a casting 1 foot 5 1/2 inches long, a 2 to 1 shaper is to have a net cutting speed of 28 feet per minute. Allow 1 1/2-inch overtravel and find the number of strokes per minute.   _____

6. A shaper with a 2 to 1 return makes 28 strokes of 1 foot length in one minute. What is the net cutting speed?   _____

7. If a 2 to 1 shaper cuts a small casting with a 6-inch stroke at the rate of 40 feet per minute net cutting speed, how many revolutions per minute are required?   _____

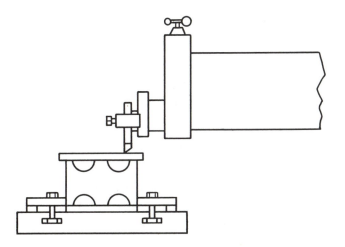

Unit 87 PRACTICAL PROBLEMS

BASIC PRINCIPLES APPLIED TO PLANER AND SHAPER WORK

- Review units 51-53 and 66 in *Basic Mathematics Simplified*.

- Apply the principles of ratio and proportion, special formulas, and handbook data in planer and shaper work to the work of the machinist by solving the Review Problems which follow.

REVIEW PROBLEMS

1. The ratchet on a 5-pitch feed screw has 50 teeth. How much feed is obtained by using a 4-tooth feed?   _____

2. What feed is represented by 1 tooth in a shaper having a 72-tooth ratchet and 3-pitch screw?   _____

3. In designing a shaper, it is found that a 60-tooth ratchet can be used. If one tooth is equal to .005 inch, what is the lead of the screw?   _____

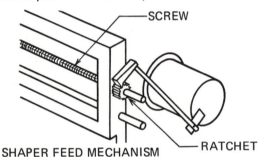

SCREW

SHAPER FEED MECHANISM   RATCHET

4. As the thread in the preceding problem could not be cut easily, a 4-pitch screw was suggested. What ratchet would be required?   _____

5. How many strokes are necessary to feed across a 2-inch piece with a 4-tooth feed where each tooth represents 7 1/2 thousandths?   _____

6. How many teeth are required to obtain a 1/8-inch feed, if the screw is 4 pitch and the ratchet has 48 teeth?   _____

7. Find the average planing speed with 35 feet per minute cutting speed and 70 feet per minute return.   _____

8. A surface 8 feet long and 14 inches wide is planed at a feed of .016 inch. One foot is allowed for overtravel and speeds of 30 and 80 feet per minute are used. Estimate the cutting time.   _____

9. When a shaper is running at 50 feet per minute with a 1-foot stroke and a return of 2 to 1, what is the cutting speed?   _____

10. A planer is set up to run 18 strokes per minute, using a .060-inch feed. What is the time required to plane a cast iron plate 18 inches wide?   _____
    What is the net cutting speed, if the length of cut is 48 inches and the   _____
    return ratio is 2 to 1?

11. What is the cutting time for two die blocks, one of which is illustrated (two blocks at a time are cut), on a 3 to 1 planer at 30 feet per minute with 3/32-inch feed? Allow 2-inch space and 3-inch over-run on each end. Disregard the time for angle cut.

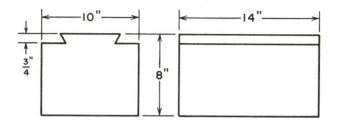

12. Estimate the total time for two roughing and one finish cut on the top, sides and ends of the cast iron plate shown in the accompanying diagram. The planer has a 2 1/2 to 1 return and cuts at 50 feet per minute with 3/16-inch feet for roughing and 3/8-inch feed for finishing. Allow 1 1/2 hours for changing and strapping to the table and allow 3 inches for overrun.

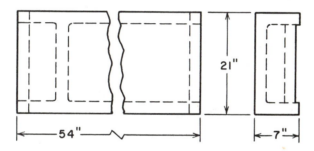

13. Determine the cutting time for a surface 18 inches wide. The cutting speed is 25 feet per minute, the return 70 feet per minute, and the feed .030 inch. A 6-foot stroke is used.

14. Estimate the time required to true the top of a 3-foot planer table which is 10 feet long. A 3/8-inch feed is used, the cut is made at 30 feet per minute, and the return is 2 1/2 to 1.

15. A planer runs at 30 feet per minute, with a 2 1/2 return stroke. What change will occur in the average speed, if the return stroke is increased to 3 to 1?

Acknowledgments

Publications Director
Alan N. Knofla

Editor-in-Chief
Marjorie Bruce

Sponsoring Editor
Elinor Gunnerson

Reviser
John G. Bradley

Production Manager
Frederick Sharer

Illustration
Bob Rome

Production Specialists
Gloria Hollister
Jean LeMorta
Lee St. Onge

FEE

95090170

677(6C1433)

TJ
1165
.B7
1973

TJ
1165
.B7

1973

7.95